D1604209

Queen Rearing

QUEEN

REARING

Harry H. Laidlaw, Jr., *and* J. E. Eckert

UNIVERSITY OF CALIFORNIA PRESS

BERKELEY, LOS ANGELES, LONDON

UNIVERSITY OF CALIFORNIA PRESS

Berkeley and Los Angeles, California

UNIVERSITY OF CALIFORNIA PRESS, LTD.

London, England

Preface

THE ULTIMATE AIM of most progressive beekeepers is to have colonies that are uniform in strength and sufficiently industrious to produce a maximum amount of honey in any period favorable to nectar secretion. They also desire to have bees that are comparatively gentle to manage, disease resistant, good pollen collectors, and economical with their stores. Colonies that are less prone to swarm are preferred, since they require less supervision. All these colony attributes, and more, are centered in the queen and in the conditions under which she is reared, other factors being equal. To obtain such excellence in beekeeping, it is important for the beekeeper to understand and to employ the fundamentals of queen rearing as the basis for a maximum measure of success in beekeeping.

Our knowledge of queen rearing has resulted from the contributions of many beekeepers and research workers in various parts of the world. We would be remiss not to mention such American contributors as Langstroth, Townsend, Alley, Doolittle, Miller, Root, Dadant, Smith, Watson, Rauchfuss, and Pellett. These and many others recorded the results of their observations in books or journals of their day, now available mainly in the larger beekeeping libraries. Because of continued interest in beekeeping, there is a demand for a ready reference to the underlying principles of bee breeding and to information on improved methods of queen rearing.

A chapter on artificial insemination is included for those who wish to make use of this tool in their research or breeding program. Absolute control of parentage is essential to a study of the manner in which the various characters of the honey bee are transmitted through successive generations, and controlled mating is quite valuable in a breeding program.

A chapter on Ailments of Queen Bees has been added to this second

edition as an aid to a better understanding of the factors that may
undermine the performance of a queen or which may prevent her
production.

We acknowledge the assistance and encouragement of Mr. M. G.
Dadant in the revision of this book and the information given by
many beekeepers and research workers since the first edition was
published.

H. H. L. and J. E. E.

Contents

CHAPTER I

The History of Queen Rearing

A REVIEW of available beekeeping literature indicates the vast interest that has been manifested in the queen honey bee and on her relation to the colony as a whole. From the first discovery that this complex insect society had a queen, observers began attempts to find the source of her influence on the vast number of her "subjects." Only within the past decade has there been a break through in a discovery of the source of that power. In the interim of many centuries, fragments of information have been assembled on her life history, methods by which she could be produced naturally and on the fundamentals that entered into the production of queens of high quality. Essential tools of bee-keeping were being discovered that made possible the full use of the potentials of the queen and her colony. Without the movable-frame hive, comb foundation, the honey extractor, or the bellows smoker, beekeeping would be, indeed, at the same stage of advancement it was in the first half of the nineteenth century. A brief summary of some of the more fundamental discoveries of the early years will give a basis for the development of the sound systems of queen rearing used at the present time.

Early Knowledge of the Queen

Our knowledge of the life history and behavior of bees has origins going back to some hundreds of years before the dawn of the Christian era. Aristotle,[1] a Greek philosopher who lived in 384–322 B.C., is given

---

[1] Haeckel, Ernest. 1896. The Evolution of Man. Vol. 1, p. 28. D. Appleton & Co., New York. Aristotle was said by Haeckel to have been aware that embryos of bees can be developed from the egg even when it has not been fertilized and so is credited with the discovery of parthenogenesis in bees.

credit for being the first to write a scientific account of the natural history of the honey bee. From his writings we learn that the bee-keepers of that day were undoubtedly aware of the presence of a queen bee in the colony. Accustomed to kings and queens or to dictators, people reasoned that a society of insects as highly developed along socialistic lines as the honey bees must also be ruled by some similar directive influence. Columella,[2] who wrote during the reigns of Tiberius and Caligula around the middle of the first century of the Christian Era, in a chapter on bees contributed the thought that the "King of the Bees . . . must be stript of his wings when he often makes eruptions with his swarm, and endeavours to run away: for having pulled off his wings, we shall retain the vagabond General as it were, with a chain at his foot: who being deprived of all means of making his escape, will not care to go without the bounds of his kingdom: for which reason he does not indeed allow the people of his dominion to ramble up and down, and wander at a greater distance from him." These early scholars did not know that she was the mother of all the bees in the colony; it was not until centuries later that this simple fact was discovered. Charles Butler,[3] an English beekeeper, appears to have been the first to bring to public attention, in 1609, the fact that the colony was indeed a "Feminine Monarchy." He thought it was ruled by a "Queen" which perpetuated the life of the colony by producing daughter queens.

Near the close of the seventeenth century, Swammerdam[4] studied the anatomy of the honey bee with the aid of a microscope. He made many remarkable discoveries, many of which have stood the test of time. Among other things, he established conclusively the sex of the queen and the drone. Around 1712, Maraldi[5] devoted considerable time to a study of bee behavior; he is credited with being the first to use glass-sided hives. From 1732 to 1744, Reaumur[5] used this device in efforts to find out how the queen mated, but he erroneously concluded that she mated with the drones while in the hive. Bonnet, of Geneva, rediscovered the phenomenon of parthenogenesis in 1740, when he showed that plant lice or aphids could reproduce without fertilization,

[2] Columella, L. J. M. 1745. Of Husbandry. Book 9, p. 396. Printed in 12 books for A. Millar.

[3] Butler, Chas. 1634. The Feminine Monarchy, or the History of Bees.

[4] Swammerdam, Jan. 1732. Biblia Naturae (A General History of Insects).

[5] Bevan, Edward. 1938. The Honeybee. Its Natural History, Physiology, and Management.

and others were led to search for the same method of reproduction in other insects.

In 1771, Schirach[6] was able to prove conclusively that queen bees could be reared from larvae in worker cells. He seems to have been the first beekeeper to use small hives for the rearing of queens, and to him might also go the honor of being the first to use baby nuclei. He proved that queens could be reared from worker larvae by shutting up a "handful of bees in a box with a small piece of comb containing eggs and maggots in worker cells." He kept the bees confined for two days, at the end of which they were found to have modified a number of the worker cells into queen cells.

While these discoveries were being made, Francis Huber,[7] a blind Swiss naturalist inspired by the memoirs of Reaumur, undertook to study bee behavior with the efficient aid of his wife and a very intelligent and able secretary, Francis Burnens. Huber wrote an account of his experiments in letters to Bonnet in 1791, who gave him every encouragement. Huber was able to prove that queens mated only on wing and when so mated could lay either worker or drone eggs at will. He showed that only drones were produced when queens were confined to their hives without mating until they began to lay. This finding confirmed the observations of Aristotle and others. Huber also repeated the experiments of Schirach and improved on them to the extent of revealing that queens could be produced from very young larvae instead of from larvae which were "three or four days old." In these experiments, Huber and his helpers placed combs containing eggs and very young larvae in queenless colonies and had them start queen cells, as had been described by Schirach. But, to prove that queens could be reared from young larvae, he had the larvae removed from the queen cells and replaced with others which were known to be only 48 hours old. Two queens emerged from five of the queen cells thus produced. In this simple experiment, Huber not only demonstrated that the bees could produce queens from young worker larvae but in doing so used the method of transferring larvae from worker cells to queen cells which is now used almost exclusively to rear queens commercially, the only difference being that he transferred larvae to nat-

[6] Schirach, M. A. G. 1787. Histoire Naturelle de la Reine des Abeilles, avec l'art de former des Essaims. Le tout Traduit de l'Allemand ou recueille par J. J. Blassiere.

[7] Huber, Francis. 1814. New Observations upon Bees. (Trans. by C. P. Dadart.) Amer. Bee Jour. Hamilton, Ill. 1926.

ural queen cells rather than to artificial queen cell cups. He also invented the leaf hive, one of the first workable comb hives in which the combs were movable, in order to facilitate his observations on the life history and habits of bees. As a means of increasing the number of his colonies, Huber divided his leaf hives and permitted the queenless portions to rear their own queens. He apparently did not realize the full significance of the possible use that could be made of the method of rearing queens he had demonstrated in his experiments.

The discoveries of Schirach and Huber paved the way for the production of queens, on a limited scale, even when most of the hives were of the immovable-frame type. Their methods persisted, with few variations or improvements, for the better part of a century.

Parthenogenesis Discovered in the Honey Bee

The next important advance in knowledge of queens was made by Dzierzon who, in 1845, published in the *Eichstadt Beinen-Zeitung* his theory that drone bees were produced without the eggs being fertilized. This observation appeared one hundred years after Bonnet discovered parthenogenesis in aphids. Dzierzon also published a book, *Theory & Practice of Bee Culture,* in 1848. He was more fortunate than Huber and some of his other predecessors in that he had two races of bees of different colors to experiment with in the final proof of his theories. He used not only the black bees of Silesia but also the Italian or yellow bee, which he introduced into Germany. It was the introduction of the latter race that enabled him to convince beekeepers that drone bees came from the unfertilized eggs of queens. When his unmated Italian queens as well as Italian queens which had mated with black drones could produce only drones which were true to the Italian race, he reasoned that all of the eggs produced in the ovaries of queens were unfertilized and that the sex of the individual bee depended on whether the egg was fertilized or not as it passed through the vagina at the time it was laid. The production of drones by egg-laying workers was additional evidence for the correctness of his theory. Further proofs to substantiate his theories were produced by Professors von Siebold and Leuckart[8,9] who demonstrated that sperms were present in eggs

---

[8] Berlepsch, The Baron of. 1861. Amer. Bee Jour. 1(6). See also "On a True Parthenogenesis in Moths and Bees," by C. T. E. von Siebold. Trans. by Dallas, 1857.

[9] Leuckart, Prof. 1861. The sexuality of bees. Amer. Bee Jour. 1(11):241–250.

when laid in worker cells by a fecundated queen but were absent in eggs laid by the same queen in drone cells. Leuckart gave a Miss Jurine credit for having first proved by dissection, in 1813, that worker bees were actually females. Baron von Berlepsch[10] did much to confirm Dzierzon's theories and collaborated with Siebold and Leuckart in their studies. These theories did not meet with ready acceptance by beekeepers and are today still disputed in some particulars.

Dzierzon devised a bar hive in which combs built on bars could be withdrawn horizontally from the back of the hive. His observations and methods of colony management and of queen rearing had a profound effect on beekeeping throughout Europe. Samuel Wagner[11] translated from the German into English Dzierzon's "Theory or the Fundamental Principles of Dzierzon's System of Bee-Culture" and had the translations printed in the *American Bee Journal* for wider distribution.

Early Progress in America

While these developments were taking place in Europe, progress was being made in the United States along almost parallel lines in many phases of the industry. In reviewing the progressive developments in the fundamentals of beekeeping, it is necessary to remember that the use of the movable-frame hive, comb foundation, the honey extractor, or even the bellows smoker came relatively late. Those who have never seen colonies handled without the aid of these essential tools may have difficulty in realizing the handicaps under which the early beekeepers operated or the changes which the discoveries have wrought. Each development came only after many years of trial-and-error efforts by many individuals in widely separated localities, and usually without the benefit of knowing what others had accomplished. Dzierzon and Langstroth, for example, were working on the development of a movable-comb hive without being aware of each other's work, and the results of their discoveries advanced the interests of beekeeping in a few short years more than had been achieved in centuries before their time.

Moses Quinby, who is considered by many to be the father of commercial beekeeping in the United States, published the first edition of

---

[10] Berlepsch, The Baron of. 1861. The Dzierzon Theory. Trans. of Berlepsch's "Apistical Letters" by Samuel Wagner, Amer. Bee Jour. 1(1–10).
[11] Phillips, E. F. 1928. Beekeeping, p. 211. The Macmillan Co.

Fig. 1. Early style hive used by J. S. Harbison of California. Rear view of brood chamber and two-pound "sections" for comb honey.

Mysteries of Beekeeping Explained in 1853, apparently without knowing of the work of Dzierzon or of Langstroth. Quinby advocated the use of swarm cells cut from colonies making preparations to swarm as a means of requeening those which had lost their queens or for providing queens for colonies made by division or by artificial swarming. He described how queen cells could be built by queenless colonies if they were given small pieces of comb containing eggs or young larvae from queenright colonies, but wrote that he had better success with cells built under the swarming impulse or in stronger colonies. He made no contribution to the advancement of queen rearing.

In the same year, Rev. L. L. Langstroth published a description of his movable-comb hive and of his system of colony management under the title *Langstroth on the Hive and the Honey Bee*. Without doubt, this was the most constructive publication on beekeeping written in the English language up to that time. Langstroth not only provided a description of the most successful movable-comb hive that has ever been invented and an outline of its advantages, but also described in detail how colony increase could be made without the benefit of natural

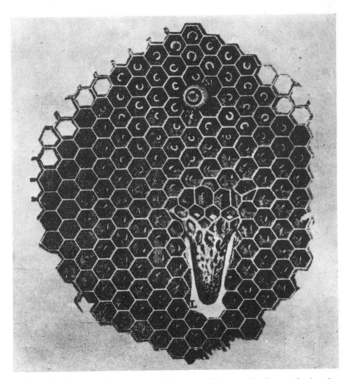

Fig. 2. A natural queen cell inserted into a hole made in the comb to receive it. From *Beekeepers Directory*, by J. S. Harbison.

swarms. His early method of rearing queens was to cut out sealed queen cells from colonies made queenless for that purpose or cells produced under the swarming impulse. He used nuclei in divided hive bodies, each nucleus consisting of one frame of brood and adhering bees. If a sufficient number of bees did not adhere to the comb, he shook additional bees into the compartment until they clustered over the brood or placed the nucleus in the location of the parent colony until a sufficient number of bees had entered. The nuclei were then given water and were kept closed from one to three days, after which each nucleus was given a sealed queen cell about ready to hatch. Langstroth called this method his nucleus system of making increase or of producing queens.

The importation of Italian bees into the United States greatly stimulated interest in beekeeping and queen rearing. Wagner, Langstroth, and Colvin received a shipment of seven queens from Dzierzon in 1859, but these are said to have died the following winter after only a few queens had been reared from them. Parsons,[11] an agent of the U.S. Division of Agriculture, is also reported to have received a shipment of Italian bees from Italy in 1859. In 1860 he made some of his stock available to Cary, to Langstroth, and to Quinby, the last of whom began to produce Italian queens in 1861. Additional shipments of Italian bees were received by various beekeepers after that date and Italian queens were soon offered for sale by a number of queen breeders.

Shipping Queens by Mail

Other developments were gradually raising queen rearing to commercial status. The first shipment of a live queen by express was made in 1863 from C. J. Robinson[12] in New York to Langstroth in Ohio. Who made the first shipment of queens by mail is not entirely clear, but the event certainly occurred within the same decade. The early shipments were made in small screened boxes; pieces of comb honey were enclosed for use as food by the bees and queen. Leakage of honey and injury of a postal clerk by a sting through a cage screen prompted a ruling by the postal authorities in 1872 to exclude bees from the mails.[12] Shipment of queens by mail did not stop entirely, however, for the ruling was not enforced at all post offices. In 1873 A. I. Root and others shipped

---

[12] Quinby, M. 1873. Bees by mail. Amer. Bee Jour. 9(2):37.

by mail pieces of combs containing eggs from Italian queens. Quinby successfully mailed a queen to the *American Bee Journal* in a cage provided with lump sugar and a wet sponge. Henry Alley[13] wrote in 1873 that he had been shipping queens successfully for six years; he supplied food by soaking a sponge in dilute honey and squeezed sufficiently to prevent any drip.

By 1878 "Dollar Italian Queens" were being advertised in *Gleanings in Bee Culture* by thirty-two beekeepers. Some queen breeders were using a water-jacketed box heated by a lamp to incubate their queen cells. A nursery cage for the cells had been invented and was used by some breeders to secure virgin queens for introduction into their nuclei.

In 1881, I. R. Good [14] advocated the use of a queen-cage candy made by mixing sugar with cold honey until firm enough to prevent any drip. Frank Benton perfected a mailing cage in 1883. In 1884, A. I. Root[15] quoted a letter from Benton indicating that the latter had shipped queens successfully in cages provisioned with a candy made from "pounded" sugar and honey. Root also stated that he had made queen-cage candy of powdered sugar and honey; he called it "Good" candy because I. R. Good had first called attention to the value of using a combination of sugar and honey for shipping bees and queens. Langstroth, as early as 1859, had given in *The Hive and the Honey Bee* a formula made by a Rev. Scholz for feeding bees in winter. It recommended mixing one pint of warmed honey with four pounds of pounded lump sugar until a stiff doughy mass was formed. Apparently this formula escaped the attention of American beekeepers interested in shipping queens until after Good had recommended a combination of sugar and honey for that purpose.

The American version of this queen-cage candy is still known as "Good" candy. At present, it is made by mixing powdered sugar with an inverted sugar syrup or a commercial inverted sugar syrup called Nulomoline. The combination of the Benton cage and the use of a soft candy which did not stick up the bees or leak from the cage provided a fairly satisfactory solution of the problem of shipping queens by mail.

---

[13] Alley, Henry. 1873. Sending bees by mail. Amer. Bee Jour. 9(5):109–110.
[14] Good, I. R. 1881. Queen cage candy. Gl. Bee Cult. 9(8):374.
[15] Root, A. I. 1884. (Comments). Gl. Bee Cult. 12(19):659–60:12(20) 728–29.

Improved Methods of Cell Building

In 1876, E. C. Larch[16] first used the term "grafting" to refer to the substitution of worker larvae for those found in naturally built queen cells. In this he duplicated the method first used by Huber, which is essentially double grafting. J. L. Davis[17] has also been credited with having used the method in 1874, when it was referred to as the "Davis Transposition Process."

In 1878, W. L. Boyd [18] suggested the feasibility of cutting out and saving naturally built queen cell cups into which newly hatched larvae could be transferred and then placed in queenless colonies. A. I. Root[18] improved on this idea by suggesting the possibility of using wooden cups to hold artificially built queen cells into which larvae could be grafted or into which the "whole bottom of the cell" could be trans-ferred with the larva. Root noted that the idea of making the cell cups artificially was suggested by "somebody" previously.

In 1880, O. H. Townsend [19] advocated the production of queen cells by cutting worker comb containing young larvae or eggs into narrow, one-cell-wide strips and fastening them to the surfaces of combs with the cells pointing downward. He placed the combs, with the strips fastened near the top bars, in queenless colonies and removed larvae from some of the cells after the bees had partially drawn out the cells. He said that he seldom left more than twenty cells at a time in each cell-building colony.

J. M. Brooks[20] improved on this method in the same year. He trimmed the strips of cells containing the eggs to one-quarter of an inch of the midrib, then fastened the strips to wooden bars which he called "cell bars" and placed them in frames for queenless colonies. The queen cells were then built from the cells containing the eggs or larvae.

Henry Alley[21] advanced the cause of queen rearing another step when, in 1883, he improved on the method of getting queen cells built.

[16] Larch, E. C. 1876. Grafting queen cells. Gl. Bee Cult. 4(3):48.

[17] Davis, J. L. 1874. Davis transposition process. Gl. Bee Cult. 2:107.

[18] Boyd, W. L. 1878. Queen cells to order. Gl. Bee Cult. 6(10):323.

[19] Townsend, O. H. 1880. How to get plenty of choice queen cells. Gl. Bee Cult. 8(7):322–323.

[20] Brooks, J. M. 1880. How to get plenty of choice queen cells another way. Gl. Bee Cult. 8(8):362.

[21] Alley, Henry. 1883. The beekeepers handy book, or twenty-two years experi-ences in queen rearing. 184 pp.

He introduced a "swarming box" and some other techniques which are worthy of note. His breeding queens were confined to small hives whose five frames were approximately five inches square. The center frame contained worker comb in which brood had been reared on one or two occasions. The other four frames were left for brood and honey. A good queen would completely fill the center comb within 24 hours after it was placed in the hive. This comb was then removed and stored in a queenless colony. When the eggs started to hatch, the comb was cut into strips having a center row of cells intact. The eggs or larvae in alternate cells in this row were destroyed and the cells cut down with a thin, hot knife, to one-quarter of an inch of the midrib. These strips were then fastened with melted wax and rosin to brood combs which had the lower half cut away on a slightly convex curve. The procedure spread the cells and prevented the queen cells from being built together.

In preparing the cell-building colonies, the bees from a required number of colonies were shaken into "swarming boxes" and held in a cool, dark place for ten to twelve hours. The brood from the colonies from which the bees were taken was divided between weaker colonies. At the end of the day the bees from the swarming boxes were transferred to broodless cell-building hives located on the original stands, and each was given a prepared comb with a strip of cells. The cell-building colonies were fed sugar syrup. When the cells were completed, they were either distributed in small four-frame nuclei or stored in nursery cages in an incubating colony. The cell builders were given the combs of brood from the next lot of colonies used to fill the swarming boxes. Alley stocked each small "fertilizing or miniature hive" with a pint of bees and kept the bees confined for two to three days in a cool, dark room. They were then placed on location, opened at nightfall and given a ripe cell or a virgin queen. The nuclei were fed sugar syrup from a feeder which was filled through a hole in the cover.

Alley also made an improved nursery cage and wrote on the care and introduction of queens as well as on many details pertaining to queen rearing.

The Doolittle System of Queen Rearing

In about 1870, G. M. Doolittle became interested in rearing queens. During the next eighteen years he gradually developed an improved system while testing all of the then-known methods. Doolittle was a keen observer, and, while he did not originate many new principles of queen rearing, he showed great ingenuity in combining the advantages of numerous methods advocated by others into a workable system. He wrote intensively for the bee journals, describing his methods of queen rearing and beekeeping.

In 1888 Doolittle published *Scientific Queen Rearing,* in which he described his experiments and the method he finally devised from the recommendations of others as well as from his own observations. This book, which is now out of print, might still be read with profit by everyone interested in rearing queens.

Doolittle utilized the method of making artificial queen cell cups and the technique of transferring young worker larvae into them. He attached twelve of the cell cups to each bar of "frame-stuff" (a portion of a bottom bar) and fastened these bars into a frame, the upper portion of which contained comb. Into these cell cups he placed a small amount of royal jelly and then transferred into them worker larvae less than 36 hours old. He experimented widely with different types of cell-building colonies and finally had the cells built in the second story of a strong colony in which the queen was confined to the lower chamber by an excluder.

When the cells were ten days old, they were placed in nuclei or in nursery cages. He experimented for a while with small nuclei whose frames were about five by six inches, but finally decided on two or three frame nuclei made up with regular-sized frames. By these methods he demonstrated that queens could be reared efficiently in quantity. This work established Doolittle's position as the founder of commercial queen rearing.

Subsequently, some refinements have been added to the techniques of queen rearing. In 1918, Frank C. Pellett, then field editor for the *American Bee Journal,* published *Practical Queen Rearing,* which summarized much of the best information available up to that time. Five years later, Jay Smith in *Queen Rearing Simplified* gave his experiences in the use of the Doolittle system of producing queens. R. E. Snodgrass's monumental textbook, *The Anatomy and Physiology of the Honeybee* appeared in 1925.

Dr. Lloyd R. Watson[22] in 1926 first demonstrated his method of artificial insemination of the queen. His instruments and methods have since been improved by others (see Chapter VII).

The package bee industry has grown steadily. It now provides hun-

---

[22] Watson, Lloyd R. 1927. Controlled mating of queen bees. Amer. Bee Journal.

dreds of thousands of colonies each year for pollination and for honey production. This development has encouraged refinements in the movement of queens and bees by mail, express, truck shipments, and by air transportation. The fundamentals of queen rearing have not changed and much still is to be learned about the factors which enter into the production and care of queen bees.

CHAPTER II

The Queen

DURING MOST of the year, a normal colony of honey bees is composed of one queen, several thousand workers, and a few hundred drones. The laying queen is longer than the workers. Her wings cover only a portion of her abdomen, which is considerably longer than the rest of her body. While her wings seem to be smaller than those of the workers, they are actually longer and broader. Her thorax is bigger than that of a worker. Its size makes it impossible for most queens to pass through a queen excluder. The drones are broader than either the queen or the workers, but are not as long as a laying queen. The queen is typically within the brood area unless the colony has been disturbed.

Relation of the Queen to the Colony

The role of the queen in the colony is a very basic one indeed. She is the mother of all members of the colony born during her "reign." Her value to the colony—and the value of the colony to man—depends on her ability to maintain an adequate force of workers and drones to perform all the functions necessary to its existence as a community of insects. The queen is the depository of all of the inherited characteristics of the colony acquired through her progenitors and through the acquisition of the sperms from the males at the time of mating. Thus the queen is responsible for the color of the bees, their industry, degree of gentleness, resistance to disease, swarming tendencies, longevity, comb-building propensities, and for many other colony attributes. By merely changing the queen in a colony, one can change many of the above characteristics within a few weeks.

A normally mated queen is capable of laying two kinds of eggs which, through the phenomenon of parthenogenesis, produce either male or female bees. Workers and queens are females; drones are males. Eggs destined to produce females are laid in worker or queen

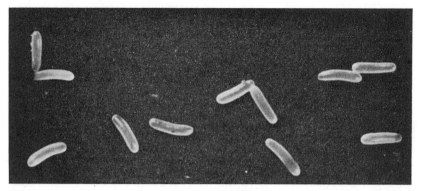

Fig. 3. Eggs of the queen honey bee.

cells; those which are to develop into drones are laid in drone cells. Unfertilized eggs usually produce only drones, but all female larvae can be developed into queens or workers, depending on the food and care given them during their early larval stages.

While the queen is the mother of a colony, she lacks "maternal instinct" and is not the controlling influence of the work of the colony. She may lay all of the eggs, but the number and kind of eggs she lays depend largely on environmental influences, such as the temperature of the brood nest and the amount and kind of food she receives from the nurse bees. The workers provide a laying queen with her food requirement when she needs it, feeding her on a mouth-to-mouth basis, in this way controlling the egg-laying activities of the queen and correlating the activities of the colony with weather, floral, and food conditions. The queen's presence does influence the "morale" of a colony, however; the behavior of a queenright colony is considerably different from one that is queenless. The queen takes no interest in the eggs she lays or in the resulting larvae. Worker bees take over the care of the brood after the eggs are laid. The queen is, therefore, an animated egg-laying machine intimately regulated by environmental conditions within and without the hive. But she is the most important single bee in the hive: without her or sufficient material from which to rear other queens, the colony is doomed to extinction.

Life History of the Queen

In the natural course of colony activities, queens are reared only under three major impulses: queenlessness, swarming, and supersedure. All

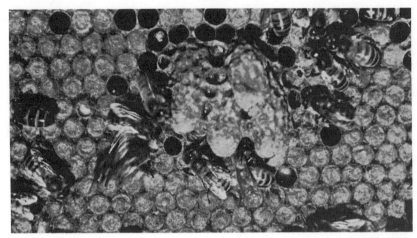

Fig. 4. Natural queen cells extending downward from the face of the comb.

larvae which hatch from the two kinds of eggs laid by the queen are
fed the same kind of food during the first two days of their existence.
Thereafter they are fed in a different manner and a different quantity
or quality of food, depending on what they are destined to become.

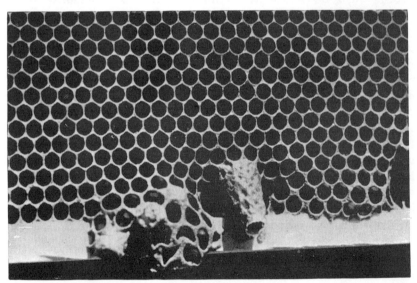

Fig. 5. Natural cell base, or "embryo cup," and cell from which a queen has
emerged.

Fig. 6. Queen cells formed from enlargements of worker cells.

Drone larvae, of course, cannot develop into anything but drones, but larvae from the fertilized eggs, the female larvae, may be developed into workers or queens.

Queens are reared in queen cells which usually extend downward from the face or edges of the comb (Fig. 4). The queen cells may be started in advance of the deposition of the egg or may be built around a cell containing an egg or larva. Those built in advance usually occur as cell bases and look something like a small acorn cup (Fig. 5). Those built around a cell are simply enlargements of the worker cell (Fig. 6). (Under some conditions, drone cells are used.) Park[1] refers to these two types of queen cells as preconstructed and postconstructed queen cells.

In an emergency, as when a laying queen is killed during the manipulation of the hive, the bees will construct a number of queen cells around larvae. Since these are built over a period of three to five days, these queen cells will contain larvae in different stages of development.

[1] Park, O. W. 1949. In: The Hive and the Honeybee. p. 41. Dadant & Sons.

Sometimes larvae of different ages are chosen by the bees at the time the cells are started. The amount of royal jelly is increased to such an extent as to float the larva out of its cell into the enlarged cell. Such cells are frequently built when a colony is being requeened and while the new queen is still confined to her cage, or when queens are purposely confined to control brood rearing.

When a colony is preparing to swarm, bees usually begin to build queen cell cups on the bottom or sides of combs some days in advance of their actual need. When the urge to swarm takes hold of the colony, the queen lays in some of the cell cups, and additional queen cells may be constructed around cells containing eggs or larvae (Fig. 7). Here again, one often finds several queen cells in varying stages of development, from newly sealed cells to those recently started. The number of cells started depends on the strength of the colony and on the intensity of the impulse to swarm. Some strains of bees build more cells than others. Carniolan bees, for example, build more queen cells than the Italians or Caucasians. Swarm cells are also found on the surface of the comb, especially in imperfections.

The supersedure impulse to rear queens takes place when the queen grows old or is injured or is unable to keep up a normal rate of egg laying. In these circumstances, the bees build queen cells, generally not more than two or three, and usually on the surface of the comb. Sometimes the failing queen lays in one or more queen cell cups. The cells are well provisioned, because of their small number, and usually pro-

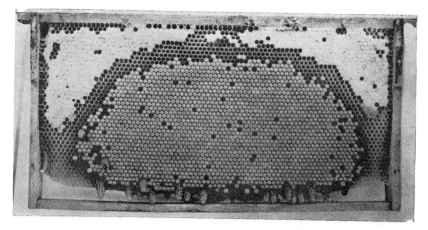

Fig. 7. Queen cells built along the bottom of a comb preparatory to swarming. Twenty-six queen cells were built on this one comb.

duce good-sized queens. The excellence of supersedure queens is frequently overrated, however. The inherited factors are fully as important as the environmental factors of food and care.

Table 1 gives the length of time spent in the developmental stages by the worker, queen, and drone. Each caste spends three days in the egg stage. As the time approaches for the egg to hatch, the shell becomes transparent and the young larva can be seen within.[2] Snodgrass[3] noted that "The young larva becomes active shortly before its emergence and curves itself in the opposite direction from the curvature of the egg, thus reversing the position it has held during its embryonic growth, and assuming that which it will maintain during most of its larval life." In the newly laid egg and during the entire course of development, the presumptive ventral surfaces of the honey bee embryo are found at the convex face of the egg, while the dorsal structures are positioned along the opposite, concave surface. Thus, as development reaches completion the larva within its egg membranes is slightly flexed in a dorsal direction, and this position is opposite to the characteristic strong ventral curving which is assumed later by the newly hatched larva.

DuPraw[4] reports that approximately an hour before hatching the honey bee larva begins active muscular movements and by a series of complex segmental contractions gradually rotates 180° around its long axis. In this process, the ventral surface of the larva comes to lie along the concave egg surface, and the larva thus acquires a slight ventral flexure even before hatching. The process of "nodding" or "bowing" which the larva undergoes in hatching is a further flexing in the larva's true ventral direction, but due to the prior rotation of the larva within the egg membranes the egg surface itself flexes in what appears as a dorsal direction. The rotating of the larva within the egg membranes is very difficult to detect in untreated eggs. Recently, however, DuPraw has found that honey bee eggs will undergo their entire three days of normal development, including hatching, while immersed in isotonic salt solutions and other liquid media. Under these conditions, the events occurring within the egg are easily visible under a low-power microscope.

Du Praw[5] has also found that the young larva produces a secretion

---

[2] Bertholf, L. M. 1925. The moults of the honeybee. Jour. Econ. Ent. 18(2):380–384.
[3] Snodgrass, R. E. 1925. The Anatomy and Physiology of the Honeybee. McGraw-Hill, New York.
[4] DuPraw, E. J. 1961. Personal communication.
[5] DuPraw, E. J. 1961. A unique hatching process in the honeybee. Trans. Amer. Micr. Soc. 80(2):185–191.

TABLE 1. LENGTH OF DEVELOPMENTAL STAGES OF THE HONEY BEE[2]

Day	Workers		Queens		Drones	
	Stages	Moults	Stages	Moults	Stages	Moults
1						
2	Egg		Egg		Egg	
3						
4	1st larval	(hatching)	1st larval	(hatching)	1st larval	(hatching)
5	2nd larval	1st moult	2nd larval	1st moult	2nd larval	1st moult
6	3rd larval	2nd moult	3rd larval	2nd moult	3rd larval	2nd moult
7	4th larval	3rd moult	4th larval	3rd moult	4th larval	3rd moult
8		4th moult		4th moult (sealing)		4th moult
	Gorging	(sealing)	Gorging			
9					Gorging	
10			Pre-pupa			(sealing)
	Pre-pupa			5th moult		
11						
		5th moult				
12					Pre-pupa	
13			Pupa			
14						
15	Pupa					5th moult
				6th moult		
16			Imago	(emerging)		
17						
18					Pupa	
19						
20						
21	Imago	6th moult (emerging)				
22						
23					Imago	6th moult
24						(emerging)

that dissolves the chorion or shell, starting at the top and proceeding downward toward the attached base. The larva bends until the head touches the bottom of the cell, by which time the chorion is almost completely dissolved. Shortly after this hatching process, the nurse bees deposit a supply of thin royal jelly on the bottom of the cell, and the larva floats on its side on its food supply. The nurse bees then mass-feed the larvae on royal jelly for two days (Fig. 8c), after which worker and drone larvae are fed at intervals while the queen larvae continue to receive a surplus of food in every well-cared-for cell. At the end of four and one-half to five and one-half days from hatching, the queen cell is sealed by the worker bees, but the queen continues to feed and gain in weight for approximately 12 hours.[6] The time of sealing the queen cell may vary a few hours with different larvae of approximately the same age.

During the larval development, the queen larva sheds its skin, or moults, four times at approximately 24-hour intervals. It then spins a cocoon of silk over the lower end and approximately three-fourths up the length of the sides of its cell, stretches out on its back with its head end toward the opening of the cell, and goes into a transformation stage which lasts approximately two days. It then casts its last larval skin, and an immature pupa appears. For the next five days the transformation from larva to adult continues, both externally and internally. Some 15 or 16 days after the egg was laid the pupal skin is shed and the imago, or adult bee, appears. Shortly thereafter the virgin queen begins to cut her way out of her cell with her mandibles. When the cap is partially cut away, she pushes it to one side and crawls out. Sometimes the cap springs back in place; it may even be fastened shut with a bit of wax by the worker bees. It is not unusual for the bees to fasten this cap in place while a worker bee is cleaning out the cell or feeding on the royal jelly, thus imprisoning the worker. However, the bees cut the queen cells down within a few days after the emergence of the queens, and often leave the bases as cell cups.

The Virgin Queen

When she emerges from her cell, the virgin queen is generally more active than the young worker. At first, she is sometimes downy and immature looking, but at other times she has all of her color and

---

[6] Oertel, E. 1930. Metamorphosis of the honeybee. Jour. Morph. & Physiol. 50:295–340.

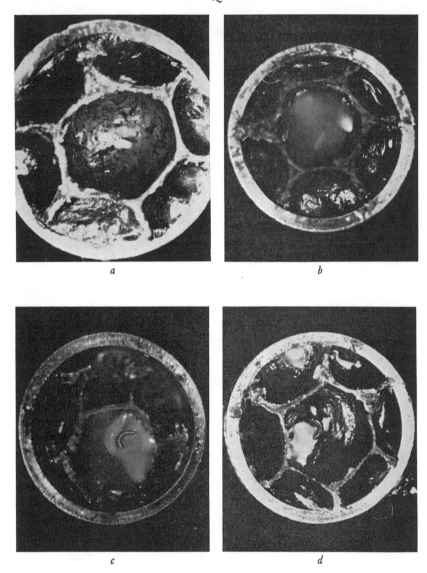

Fig. 8. Hatching of the egg and early feeding of larvae in worker cells. *a*, egg; *b*, egg surrounded with royal jelly prior to hatching; *c*, larva about 12 hours old and abundantly supplied with royal jelly; *d*, larva about 12 hours old and scantily supplied with royal jelly.

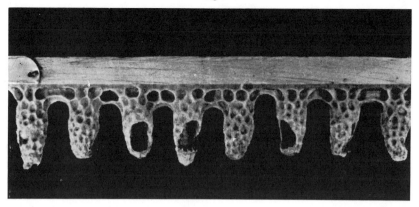

Fig. 9. Queen cells, produced by the Doolittle method, which have been destroyed by a virgin queen.

vitality enough to fly or to fight. Under some conditions the bees may delay the emergence of the young queens for some hours, and during the last few hours queens remain in their cells they not infrequently "challenge" each other by emitting shrill "piping" sounds which, at times, can be heard outside of their hives. A newly emerged queen may accept food from a nurse bee or may take honey from an open cell. Bees have been seen to feed queens through a small opening in their cells, and on occasion the queen may stop her work of cutting off the capping and stick her tongue through as if to "ask" for food of an attendant bee.

The first concern of the virgin queen is to seek out rivals either in or outside of their cells. She destroys numerous queen cells by cutting a small hole in their sides and inserting her long curved sting into the unfortunate inmate (Fig. 9). During this task, the worker bees seem to give considerable assistance in tearing down the cells and in dragging out the inmates. Virgin queens pay little attention to unsealed queen cells and the bees soon discontinue their construction.

The abdomen of the virgin queen shrinks somewhat after the first few hours, due largely to the discharge of liquid waste materials. She may thereafter be found in any part of the brood nest, resting or pushing her way among the bees. She is more excitable than a laying queen and may fly from the combs or hide under a mass of bees if the colony is disturbed.

Mating of the Queen

The virgin queen mates with the drone while on wing in the open, never in the hive, and seldom, if ever, inside of any enclosure. Within three to five days after she has emerged from her cell, she may take one or more orientation flights to mark the location of her hive and mating sometimes occurs on these flights. Under average flight conditions, however, weather factors being favorable, the queen will take her nuptial flight sometime between the fifth and fourteenth day after emerging from her cell. If a virgin queen is confined to her hive by unfavorable weather conditions for a period of approximately three weeks without an opportunity for a mating flight, or if she is unsuccessful in her attempts to mate during this time, she may start to lay and thus become a drone layer. Many commercial queen breeders will destroy all virgin queens which have failed to mate within fourteen days after emergence, for they believe that queens which mate later tend to be inferior layers.

During her mating flights the queen may fly a considerable distance from her hive, if drones are not plentiful, before she is successful. Experience has indicated that it may be necessary to locate a mating yard several miles from other colonies to assure purity of mating under natural conditions. The location of mating yards on Kelley's Island and Pelee Island in Lake Erie, by the United States and Canadian Governments, respectively, is an excellent example of an attempt to influence matings. Mating flights average from ten to twenty minutes, being longer in the spring than in the summer when the weather is warmer and drones are more numerous. Very few reports have been recorded of queens being observed in the act of mating, but it is known that the sex organs of the drone are detached * from its body during or following the act and sometimes remain attached to the queen on her return to the hive. This telltale "sign" of mating may remain attached to the body of the queen for some hours. A few sperms at a time are released to fertilize eggs which are to become females. Woyke and Ruttner[7] believe the "mating sign" or bulb separates along the surface of a preformed layer of chitin in the bulb wall and that the fully

---

* Possibly the severance is accomplished by the queen's mandibles.

[7] Woyke, J. and F. Ruttner. 1958. An anatomical study of the mating process in the honey bee. Bee World 38(1):3–18.

everted endophallus separates undamaged from the bulb, and with it the separation of the queen and drone is accomplished. This concept still leaves unexplained how the bulb is removed prior to subsequent matings on the same flight.

For many years it was considered that queens mated only once in their life time, but recent observations have revealed that some queens mate more than once before they begin to lay. In describing multiple matings, Roberts has observed:

The 40 queens made a total of 88 flights, the number ranging from one to five per queen. All queens returned once or twice with the mating sign. Nonmating flights lasted from 4 to 19 minutes, with an average of 11 minutes. Mating flights lasted from 5 to 21 minutes, averaging 14.4 minutes. Nineteen queens mated on their first flight and nine of these did not leave the hive again. Nine queens left the hive only twice and mated on both flights. Twenty-one mated only once and nineteen mated twice. Two of the single-mated queens made additional flights after once mating. Of the queens mating twice, seventeen mated on successive days and two had an interval of one day between matings.[8]

Queens have seldom been seen to leave the hive after they have started to lay, except to leave with the swarm.

Oviposition

THE LAYING OF EGGS

Within two or three days after mating, the queen begins to deposit eggs in worker cells, each egg being fastened by the small end with a sticky substance to the bottom of the cell. Queens which have not mated or are laying abnormally will frequently lay two or more eggs in a cell and sometimes fasten them to the sides of the cell. A good queen will lay regularly in an area on one side of a comb and then lay in the opposite side, gradually extending her brood area to the adjacent combs. She first inserts her head into a cell, as if to inspect it, and then either passes on to another cell or inserts her abdomen in the cell and extrudes the egg so that it is attached to the bottom of the cell. All eggs which the queen lays have a small amount of adhesive material on the small, or caudal, end (Fig. 10).

---

[8] Roberts, William G. 1944. Multiple mating of queen bees proved by progeny and flight tests. Gl. Bee Cult. 72(6):255–59, 303.

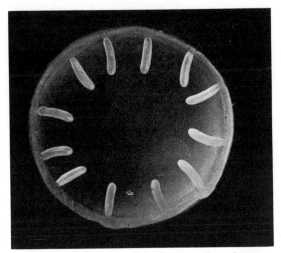

Fig. 10. Eggs stuck against inner edge of queen cell cup to illustrate the adhesive nature of the small end of the egg.

THE PRODUCTION OF EGGS

The two ovaries of the queen, composed of a number of tubules called ovarioles, are located in the anterior portion of her abdomen. The total number of tubules varied from 260 to 373 in one study made on 280 queens.[9] The primary egg cells are located in the upper end of each tubule. As it progresses down its tubule toward the base of the ovary, where all tubules open into an oviduct, the egg cell gradually develops at the expense of accompanying nurse cells. The egg shell, or chorion, is formed when the cell reaches its full size and just before it passes into the oviduct. An opening through the chorion in the larger end of the egg, the micropyle, provides for entrance of the sperm. Approximately two days elapse from the time the egg is started by the primary egg cell until it is completed.

A normal queen, under favorable colony and environmental conditions, lays an average of some 1,500 eggs each day, although some brood counts made by early workers indicated that queens have laid as many as 3,000 eggs a day for a short period of time. The egg-laying rate, as stated previously, depends on the strength of the colony, temperature of

[9] Eckert, J. E. 1934. Studies in the number of ovarioles in queen honey-bees in relation to body size. Jour. Econ. Ent. 27(3):629–635.

the hive, amount of available space, and amount and kind of food fed to the queen by the nurse bees. Some queens, for some unknown reason, may at first lay somewhat irregularly, but after a few days a well-mated queen lays an increasing number of eggs daily until she reaches the peak of her potential. In small nuclei or in colonies with limited egg-laying space, a queen may lay two or more eggs in some cells. As the numerical strength of the colony increases, this trait disappears. If a queen is imperfectly inseminated, she frequently lays a number of drone eggs in worker cells. This trait also is manifested as the spermatozoa become exhausted, although a well-mated queen normally may lay drone or worker eggs "at will" for several years.

The Fertilization of the Egg

As the egg passes down the oviduct and into the vagina it passes a point where the canal from the spermatheca opens into the vagina. Here a valvefold is situated and causes the large end of the egg to brush past the opening of the canal. If the egg is to be fertilized, a number of sperms are released from the spermatheca. These pass down the spermathecal canal and one or more enter the small opening in the chorion, whereupon one unites with the nucleus of the egg, thus effecting fertilization. If the egg is not to be fertilized, the valvefold is probably lowered as the egg passes through the vagina, and the egg is laid unfertilized. All eggs produced in the ovaries of the queen are unfertilized and will develop into drones unless they are fertilized as they pass through the vagina.

At one time it was reasoned by a number of writers that the curvature of the abdomen or the pressure exerted on the queen's abdomen by the sides of worker cells caused her to lay eggs which developed into females, while the larger drone cells did not produce this critical pressure. This theory can be discounted in many ways. Queens occasionally lay in queen cell cups, whose openings are usually larger and depths more shallow than those of worker cells. Yet she lays eggs which develop into female larvae. Queens also lay worker eggs in worker cells before they have been fully completed and before the cell walls can cause any pressure on the abdomen. A normally mated young queen seems loath to lay drone eggs for a number of weeks after she begins to lay, and when confined to a comb containing only drone cells she may lay eggs which will produce female larvae (Fig. 11).

Queens lay worker or drone eggs in a systematic manner and accord-

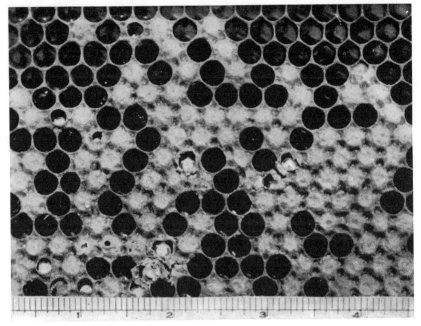

Fig. 11. Worker pupae reared in drone cells.

ing to the influence of environmental conditions. So it is now accepted that a normally mated queen lays fertilized or unfertilized eggs according to the needs or environmental influences of the colony, and similarly lays them in the proper cells. She generally, for example, lays a few drone eggs in the spring far enough in advance of the swarming period to provide drones of proper maturity to assure the mating of the virgin queen following the issuance of the first swarm.

Classification and Judging of Queens

Purebred Queens

A queen that produces uniformly marked workers and drones may be considered to have originated from a purely bred queen mother and to have mated with drones of similar race. Since a queen mates only in flight, the type of drone with which she mates depends largely on chance, and if she mates more than once the chance of her producing workers of mixed colors is enhanced. It is possible for a multiple-mated queen to produce bees which are uniform in color for a period of time and then produce some workers of a different color. This might occur, for example, if an Italian queen mated first with a Caucasian drone and then with an Italian.

The mating of a queen does not influence the color of her drones since they originate from unfertilized eggs; consequently, the color of the drones produced by a queen is a good indication of her purity of breeding, but not of her mating.

CLASSIFICATION OF QUEENS

Queens are usually classified as untested, tested, select tested, and breeders. *Untested* queens are those which are sold soon after they begin to lay. If queens are held in their nuclei until their bees emerge, so that the producer can determine their purity of mating, they are said to be *tested*. *Select-tested* queens have been held in producing colonies until the producer can judge them not only for purity of mating, but also for disease resistance, productivity, gentleness, and other characteristics. Queens to be used as *breeders* are kept until it is known whether their daughter queens are capable of producing colonies with most of the characteristics desired by the buyer. This requires keeping the prospective breeder queens and several of their daughters at the head of producing colonies for one or two seasons, with records of honey production, industry, gentleness, wintering qualities, swarming propensities, resistance or susceptibility to various brood and adult diseases, as well as other qualities.

Most queens sold commercially fall in the untested class, but if these are produced by a breeder who attempts to control the types of drones in the area in which the queens are reared a large percentage of the queens will be purely mated and satisfactory. The longer the queens are held in their nuclei or in producing colonies the more costly they become to the producer.

FACTORS AFFECTING THE VALUE OF A QUEEN

The value of a queen depends, largely, on her ability to lay a sufficient number of eggs to maintain a strong colony appropriate to the various seasons of the year. And since the queen is responsible for the various characteristics of the colony, some of her value relates to them. But with the inheritance of suitable qualities and with proper environmental conditions, the value of a colony depends mainly on its population.

The factors which influence the fecundity of a queen are numerous and closely associated with each other. The size of the queen depends, for example, largely on the amount and quality of food received by the larva during its developmental period. The food factor in turn is dependent on the number of bees of the right age, the availability and quality of the pollen and honey from which the royal jelly is elaborated by the nurse bees, and the number of queen cells the bees have to feed. As previously stated, all larvae are mass-fed during the first two days, but afterwards the worker larvae receive food only at intervals while those destined to become queens are mass-fed during their entire larval existence. Under favorable conditions, queen larvae always have an abundance of royal jelly and a surplus is left in the bottom of their cells after emergence.

The amount of food and the size of the resulting queen depend to a considerable extent on the age of the larva at the time the queen cell is started. While queens can be reared from larvae which are approximately 72 hours old, those reared from larvae over 48 hours old are progressively smaller than queens reared from younger larvae. Queens reared experimentally from larvae 36 and 48 hours old were not appreciably smaller in size than those reared from still younger larvae.[9] Queens reared from 24-hour larvae are as desirable as any reared from younger larvae, providing they have had an abundance of royal jelly during their first 24-hour period.

The factors of shape and size vary about as much in queens as in other animals. A queen may be long and slender or she may be short or stubby, or she may be of average or large proportions. The number of ovarioles in the ovaries of queens do not vary in direct proportion to external size. Ovaries do vary in length in queens of different sizes, but no correlation was found between the number of ovarioles and the amount of brood produced by queens included in one study of this subject.[9] Nor was any significant variation evident in the number of ovarioles in queens reared from larvae which were 12, 24, 36, 48, 60 and 72 hours old at the time of transfer to queen cell cups. The size of the queen is some indication of the amount of food that she received during her developmental period, and may be some indication of her stamina.

How to Judge Queens

The performance of a queen and of her colony is probably the best criterion for judging her excellence. If a queen is prolific enough to maintain a suitably strong colony, and if the colony has a majority of the characteristics desired in a producing colony, then the queen is a good one regardless of her size and looks. One should judge queens by looking at the brood and the number of bees in the colony rather than at the queen herself. The brood should be concentrated in a rather condensed brood area and should have very few empty cells scattered among the sealed brood. The presence of drone brood in worker cells among normal worker brood is evidence of a poor or failing queen. The amount of brood should be consistent with the strength of the colony, the availability of pollen and honey, and the environmental conditions of the season.

A young queen is more active than an old queen and is more likely to push under a group of bees or to crawl around on the comb and hide when the colony is disturbed. She is also brighter looking because the hairs on her thorax and abdomen have not been rubbed off. As she ages, she moves more slowly (extremely old queens may also tremble in movement), she becomes more shiny as hair is rubbed off portions of her body, and her abdomen grows darker and more transparent. For use as a breeder, an old queen may be just as good as, or even better than, a younger queen, for age may indicate the possibility of an inherent vitality and longevity which younger queens have not had time to demonstrate. But, whether a queen is young or old, it is best that she be well proportioned, carry her wings folded over a portion of her abdomen, and move regularly over the combs, using all six legs in a normal manner. The abdomen should be symmetrically shaped. A majority of well-bred queens have a uniform color over most of the dorsal part of the abdomen, while the ventral side of the abdomen is usually lighter in color.

The Food of Queens

Origin

The food of bees comes from three natural sources, nectar, pollen and water. From these main constituents, the worker bees elaborate the food they need for themselves and for their queens, drones, and developing brood. Nectar provides the carbohydrates, some minerals, a portion of the enzymes and vitamins, and some of the water needed for the production of energy and for the building of various elements of the cells of the body. Pollen provides the only natural source of protein for the bees. It also contains vitamins, minerals, and fats. Water dissolves and dilutes honey, provides some minerals, and serves to maintain a balance of water in the blood and body tissues. Adult bees can maintain themselves on honey or sugar syrup alone, but require pollen, or a suitable substitute, for the production of brood food.

Brood food originates from the digestion of pollen and honey in the digestive tract of the worker bee. The materials are broken down into simpler compounds by various enzymes, and are absorbed into the blood stream. A pair of glands located in the head region of worker bees, known as pharyngeal or brood-food glands, take from the blood the constituents needed to produce a secretion which is passed down through their ducts to the mouth cavity near the base of the tongue. This secretion, together with the addition of suitable amounts of carbohydrates and possibly of secretions from other glands as well, is known as royal jelly. As it appears in the brood cells, the secretion is milky white in color and of the consistency of thick cream. If removed from the cells and kept at room temperature, it turns slightly yellowish. It can be kept for a year or more without deterioration if held at a temperature of 35°F (2°C). Royal jelly kept in a deep freeze at 0°F showed little deterioration for periods up to several years.[10]

AGE AT WHICH BEES PRODUCE ROYAL JELLY

The ability to produce royal jelly varies with the physiological age of the worker bees. Under normal conditions young workers are capable of producing a maximum amount of royal jelly between the fifth and fifteenth days after they have emerged from their cells. The pharyngeal glands of younger bees are not fully developed, and they deteriorate in older bees. However, the "age" of the bee depends more on its physical development and physiological condition than on time alone. Bees just emerging from a winter period of several months, for example, can still produce sufficient royal jelly to rear queen and worker brood. A colony made up only of old workers can still rear brood but the resulting individuals frequently are undersized.

---

[10] Smith, M. V. 1959. The production of royal jelly. Bee World 40(10):250–254.

THE COMMERCIAL PRODUCTION OF ROYAL JELLY

Smith has described a method of producing royal jelly in quantity for research purposes. A small number of beekeepers throughout the world raise royal jelly to supply a limited demand for therapeutic purposes. The fundamentals are the same as those incorporated in the production of good queen cells for rearing queens. Thorough knowledge of honey bees and their behavior is required.

A strong queenright colony can care for 45 grafted cells a day. At the end of the third day, the grafted cells are removed from the cell-building colonies, cut down to approximately the level of the royal jelly within by means of a sharp, hot, thin-bladed knife, and the larvae removed gently with fine forceps. The royal jelly is then removed by suction, with the vacuum arranged so the royal jelly is deposited in a bottle or collection tube of glass. As used by Smith, the tube is three-quarters to one inch in diameter, six to eight inches long, and open at both ends. One end is closed with a solid cork that fits snugly into the tube. In the other end, a cork is fitted with two glass tubes, one connected with the vacuum and the other being used to remove the royal jelly from the cells. The tube can be completely emptied by removing the latter cork and forcing the solid one through the length of the tube.

The royal jelly can be strained of bits of wax and moulted skins of the larvae by forcing the royal jelly through a 100-mesh nylon cloth held tightly across the end of the tube. The jelly should then be re-frigerated immediately.

The cell cups can be used over again. Plastic cups work as well as those made of beeswax.

CHEMICAL COMPOSITION OF ROYAL JELLY

Various investigators have found by chemical and biological analyses that royal jelly is a complex substance which varies, in some respects, according to the age and type of larva to which it is fed. It contains abundant tissue-building proteins and energy-producing carbohydrates and fats, an appreciable amount of "B" vitamins, moisture, and other materials which have not been determined. Planta, one of the first to investigate the chemical nature of royal jelly, thought that the bees added honey and pollen after the fourth day, but more recent investigations tend to show that its composition remains rather constant, particularly so when taken only from queen cells. Pollens found in royal jelly from queen cells may be accidental inclusions. It is quite probable, also, that the differences in the chemical constituents of royal jelly, as determined by different investigators, may be due to variations in the chemical composition of the pollen and honey from which the different samples were made.

Haydak[11] made a comprehensive review of investigations into the chemical composition of the larval food of bees and the reader is referred to his article for further references on this subject. Two tables will suffice to indicate the chemical composition of royal jelly as determined by Melampy and Jones[12] and by Haydak and Vivino.[13]

Melampy and Jones collected the royal jelly for their experiments over a period of six months from queen cells which contained larvae between three and four days old. The average of their eight samples had the following chemical composition: moisture, 66.05%; protein, 12.34%; total lipid (fat), 5.46%; total reducing substance, 12.49%; ash (minerals), 0.82%; and undetermined, 2.84%. They considered that the total reducing substance in royal jelly is an index of the carbohydrates present.

QUEEN-CAGE CANDY

In the commercial production of queen bees, considerable difficulty has been encountered to secure a food that will sustain them without ill effects during the time they are confined to their cages. The best food *per se* is honey, and this was tried first. But it was discarded because the small combs were prone to leak from the package or smear up the bees. Then a combination of honey and powdered sugar was used, mixed together until it formed a firm candy that would hold its shape in hot weather. Honey is no longer used as a constituent of queen-cage candy because of the possible danger of spreading American foulbrood should any honey be used which came from an infected

[11] Haydak, Mykola H. 1943. Larval food and development of castes in the honeybee. Jour. Econ. Ent. 33(5):778–92.

[12] Melampy, R. M. and Jones, D. Breese. 1939. Chemical composition and vitamin content of royal jelly. Proc. Soc. Exp. Biol. & Med. 41:382–88.

[13] Haydak, M. H. & Vivino, A. E. 1950. The changes in the thiamine, riboflavin, niacin, and pantothenic acid content in the food of female honeybees during growth with a note on the vitamin activity of royal jelly and bee bread. Ann. Ent. Soc. Amer. 43:361–367, tables 1–2.

TABLE 2. CHEMICAL COMPOSITION OF ROYAL JELLY[11]

Sample	Moisture %	Dry matter %	Protein %	Total lipid %	Total reducing substance %	Ash %	Undetermined %
1	66.50	33.50	13.38	5.03	11.16	.88	3.05
2	66.38	33.62	12.38	5.92	12.99	.82	1.51
3	65.86	34.14	12.66	5.27	12.00	.81	3.40
4	65.55	34.45	12.16	5.51	11.61	.81	4.36
5	67.42	32.58	11.97	5.26	12.10	.82	2.43
6	66.44	33.56	11.75	5.51	12.70	.76	2.84
7	64.63	35.37	11.78	5.83	14.06	.82	2.88
8	65.60	34.40	12.63	5.38	13.27	.86	2.26
Av.	66.05	33.95	12.34	5.46	12.49	.82	2.84

TABLE 3. CHEMICAL COMPOSITION OF THE LARVAL FOOD OF FEMALE HONEY BEES[12]

Age of larvae days	Moisture	Dry Matter	Nitrogen	Protein Nx6.25	Fat	Ash	pH
Per cent in fresh matter							
Royal Jelly							
1	65.37	34.63	2.24	14.00	2.63	1.19	4.15
2	69.17	30.83	2.41	15.06	1.73	0.91	4.10
3	69.88	30.12	2.44	15.25	4.86	0.79	4.20
4	69.70	30.30	2.24	14.00	5.68	0.70	4.15
5	67.58	32.42	2.58	16.13	4.92	0.76	4.19
Sealed	68.32	31.68	2.94	18.38	3.99	0.75	4.15
Larval Food of Workers							
1–2	73.51	26.49	3.32	20.75	4.69	1.07	4.00
3–5	64.90	35.10	2.83	17.69	2.06	0.58	3.90
Per cent in dry matter							
Royal Jelly							
1			6.47	40.43	7.59	3.34	
2			7.82	48.85	5.61	2.95	
3			8.10	50.63	16.13	2.63	
4			7.39	46.20	18.74	2.31	
5			7.93	49.75	15.18	2.34	
Sealed			9.28	58.01	12.59	2.37	
Larval food of workers							
1–2			12.53	78.33	17.70	4.04	
3–5			8.06	50.39	5.87	1.65	

colony. (Some beekeepers still use this type of candy in their own cages, selecting a light-colored, well-ripened honey which they know was produced in an area entirely free of foulbrood.)

The candy which is now used universally for the commercial shipment of queens is the "Good" candy mentioned earlier. It was first made in Europe by a Mr. Scholz, and so is also called "Scholz" candy. It is made by mixing invert sugar syrup and powdered sugar in approximately a 1:2½ or 1:3 ratio. The powdered sugar is first stirred into the sugar syrup; when the mixture becomes too thick to stir, it is kneaded as more powdered sugar is added, until a firm candy is formed that will not run out of the candy compartment in the queen cage.

Beekeepers sometimes invert their own sugar solution by adding cream of tartar. But if this is not correctly done, the resulting candy will not be satisfactory. Much of the candy is now made from a commercial invert sugar known as Nulomoline, which is produced without the use of acid, and which is mixed with powdered sugar, as described. Some beekeepers also add a few drops of glycerine, which tends to prevent the candy from drying out. Sugar without starch is preferable to that containing a small amount of starch, but starch-free sugar is generally lumpy and the lumps hard to pulverize to a suitable fineness.

Queen-cage candy should be left to stand for some hours before using in order to insure proper consistency. It should not be hard and dry nor soft and sticky. In hot weather, more powdered sugar is required than in cooler seasons. If properly made, the candy can be stored in an air-tight container for a considerable period.

While queens and bees can be shipped through the mails for a period of a week or more when confined to queen-cage candy, they will not survive for a much longer period unless they have access to water to offset the dehydrating effects of the sugars. The small amount of starch in powdered sugar has little, if any, ill effects on the workers or queens. The main ingredient which is lacking in queen-cage candy, as made at present, is an adequate amount of moisture.

POLLEN SUPPLEMENTS

Considerable interest has been shown in the feeding of pollen supplements as a means of stimulating brood rearing during periods of pollen shortage or to increase colony strength for specific purposes. The utility of various compounds has been investigated by numerous research workers and beekeepers, and the beekeeping literature contains many articles on this subject. The most commonly used supplement to natural pollen is soybean flour, with a low fat content, and powdered yeast. These are frequently fed dry by mixing the flour and yeast in the proportions of nine to one and placing the mixture in a box with a lid sufficiently ajar to admit bees but to keep out wind and rain. Another method is to make a cake by mixing honey or heavy sugar syrup with the yeast and soybean flour so that the dough is firm enough to hold its shape. When fed to the bees, the cake is placed on the top bars immediately above the brood area and covered with waxed paper.

Pollen traps are sometimes used on populous colonies to collect pollen pellets from the legs of bees during heavy pollen production. This pollen is then dried and stored in an air-tight container (so that the wax moth and various other insects will not feed on it) until it is needed for stimulative feeding. The dried pollen pellets can be moistened with water and then mixed with four parts of soybean flour and sufficient honey or heavy sugar syrup to make a soft but firm cake. The addition of sulfathiazole or terramycin (not both) will aid in preventing AFB. The medicant is dissolved in the water used to make the syrup, using one-half level teaspoon of sodium sulfathiazole or one and one-half teaspoons of TM-25 to each pound of sugar. The bees are supplied with the pollen cakes as long as they do not have access to a plentiful supply of fresh pollen. TM-25 is used only if EFB is to be a factor.

Most queen breeders, however, prefer to collect combs of pollen from producing colonies for their cell builders. There is no substitute which will take the place of natural pollen gathered by the bees or stored by them in their combs. It is usually considered that it takes one comb of pollen and one of honey to produce two combs of brood.

CHAPTER III

The Production of Queen Cells

QUEENS ARE PRODUCED in one way only: the attending bees feed the developing female larvae suitable food and in quantities sufficient to develop the characteristics peculiar to the queen. The larvae are sensitive to variations in this feeding, and inadequate feeding during any part of the feeding stage may interfere with the full development of the queen's characteristics. Bees feed the developing larvae properly only when an abundance of nurse bees are present, and when they have a good income of nectar, honey or sugar syrup, and pollen. A shallow super of honey is sometimes placed on the bottom board in lieu of feeding syrup.

Environmental Factors Necessary for the Production of Good Cells

In common with the worker bee, the queen develops from a fertilized egg. The egg hatches in three days and a small amount of food is provided at the time of hatching. Food is then supplied until the cell is sealed. Larvae which hatch from eggs deposited in queen cells, or which were otherwise selected very early by the bees to become queens, normally receive a greater abundance of royal jelly, or brood food, during the first two days than do larvae hatched from eggs laid in worker cells and destined to become workers. Otherwise, the food appears to be much the same during this first two-day period. This period is critical, and a scarcity of food for even a few hours might prevent the resulting queen from reaching full physiological development. That the larvae which are hatched in queen cells normally receive a greater abundance of food during the first two days than even well-fed worker larvae does not necessarily mean, however, that they are actually better fed during this period, for there is a limit to the amount of food the larva can consume. But it is possible and even probable that larvae hatched in worker cells and fed *sparingly,* as judged by the amount of brood food in the cell (Fig. 8D), are underfed and will produce queens inferior to those adequately fed from the time of hatching.

In the production of good queen cells, one would do well to approximate the conditions which exist in nature when a strong colony produces cells under the swarming impulse. At such times the colony is usually at its peak of strength numerically, thus insuring an abundance of food, nurse bees, wax builders, ventilators, and fielders. The combs in the hive are well filled with honey, pollen, and brood. The incoming nectar and pollen creates a condition favorable to the production of both wax and brood food. The crowded condition of the brood nest and the restriction in the available space to rear brood result in an overabundance of nurse bees and the production of royal jelly in excess of the colony's needs. Wax builders are stimulated to wax production by the evaporation and storage of nectar and by the increased heat of the hive. Drone production is in full swing and mature drones are present in numbers. This combination of factors generally results in the preparation of numerous queen cell cups in which the queen will lay, in the construction of queen cells, and, finally, in swarming, unless unfavorable weather intervenes.

These conditions are not always present when queens are reared by the supersedure impulse or under the emergency of queenlessness. In either of these cases, the colony may be weak or the other environmental conditions may not be favorable. The main factor in favor of queens reared under the supersedure impulse is in the small number of cells which are usually produced. Under the emergency impulse, as when a queen is removed from a colony, the bees may rear as many cells as they would under the swarming impulse. One of the main disadvantages of this reaction is that if the bees are left to their own devices they may construct cells around larvae which are too old to produce the best of queens. If the emergency occurs when natural conditions are unfavorable, the resulting queen larvae may be poorly fed.

If one wishes to rear queens at a more convenient time than during the swarming season, it is necessary to simulate or to improve on natural factors which are present when cells are built naturally under optimum conditions. A colony of bees can be strengthened by the addition of the required number of young bees and emerging brood from other colonies. The production of brood food can be increased by feeding a heavy sugar syrup or dilute honey in the absence of a nectar flow but when there is an abundance of pollen in the combs. The feeding of a pollen supplement (Fig. 12) along with sugar syrup also stimulates brood rearing and an increase of brood food when unsealed brood is present.

If this stimulative feeding is started in early spring, a queen will increase her egg laying and produce drones earlier, and the colony will be ready to rear queen cells earlier than it would do otherwise. The same stimulative methods will also encourage a queenless colony to produce more brood food if young larvae which need feeding are supplied. The response of either the queenright or the queenless colony to build good queen cells will continue as long as the relation between food and the colony population of bees of suitable age is maintained.

Sugar syrup or dilute honey is fed continuously to cell-building colonies to simulate a nectar flow and to stimulate the bees to produce wax. Good queen cells should be large, well formed, and sculptured

Fig. 12. Supplying pollen to a colony by means of a pollen-soybean cake. The cake must be placed immediately above the brood area.

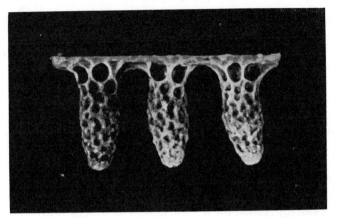

Fig. 13. Large, well-formed queen cells. These cells, produced by the Doolittle method, have heavy wax bases to aid in handling them.

(Fig. 13), and are more likely to have these characteristics when there is an adequate number of young bees to secrete wax. Beeswax is elaborated from carbohydrates by the wax glands of worker bees. These glands reach their greatest productivity during the second and third weeks after the bee emerges from its cell. Older bees can produce wax, but with greater difficulty and less abundantly than this age group. The processing of nectar or sugar syrup stimulates the production of wax and better queen cells. If the young bees have to retain a supply of sugar syrup or of nectar during the time they are inverting the sugars and evaporating the excess moisture, for want of available cells in which to store it they involuntarily produce more wax. Too much crowding, however, can cause the bees to build excessive burr comb or to enclose the cells in a web of comb. The temperature of the hive can be regulated artificially by supplying additional heat, by reducing the size of the entrance, or by crowding the bees into a limited space. If the cell-building colony is strong enough in bees, it will maintain a satisfactory temperature for queen cell production.

The fewer queen cells a colony has to build the better they will build them, within certain limits. The location of the cells in the center of the cluster of bees will insure a more even distribution of heat and a greater concentration of nurse bees. Too much crowding and a lack of adequate ventilation, however, will cause many of the bees to leave the brood nest and will result in the production of poorer cells. Additional ventilation and suitable clustering space for the field bees and ventilators can be provided by increasing the depth of the space beneath the bottom bars of the lower brood chamber by adding a two-inch rim to the depth of the bottom board. This also makes it easier to attach a feeder to the back or side of the hive at the level of the bottom board.

The production of royal jelly calls for the consumption of large amounts of pollen. For best results, combs of pollen should be placed in the same hive body with the cells which are being built. Most queen breeders prefer to take combs of pollen from other colonies to place in their cell builders rather than to feed pollen supplements.

Another important factor in the production of good cells is the provision of suitable brood for the nurse bees to feed in order to continue the production of royal jelly. This can be accomplished by giving the bees young grafted larvae every third or fourth day or just before one lot of cells is sealed. Strong cell builders can be given a comb containing some young larvae next to the frame containing the queen cells. This tends to attract more nurse bees to the compartment in which the queen cells are located when the cell builder occupies two or three stories.

The location of the cells in the second story of a two- or three-story colony will assure a more even temperature and a greater number of younger bees. The older bees, which are of no material help in the production of brood food or in the secretion of wax, except through their efforts in bringing in nectar, water and pollen, congregate in the lower story.

Manipulative Practices

A beekeeper who wishes to produce one or a thousand queens can get bees to build queen cells when his cell builders are activated by one of the three impulses previously mentioned, swarming, supersedure, or queenlessness. If only a few cells are desired during the year and there is no particular urge to have them at any particular time, naturally built queen cells can be used when they are available. If production of a number of queens at different times during the year or continuously during the major portion of the brood rearing season is desired, then it will be necessary to stimulate the colonies by forcing them into a condition of swarming or of queenlessness or by raising brood above a queen excluder in a queenright colony. Whichever method is used, all of the essential factors for the production of good cells must be present to insure queens of the desired quality.

The kinds of manipulative practices resorted to by the beekeeper to induce the bees to build queen cells are immaterial if they insure the proper feeding and care of the larvae. There are, however, several manipulative practices which appear to provide the necessary food and other care and are of a very practical nature.

The queen rearing methods used by the beekeeper who produces queens in small numbers and those used by the beekeeper who produces queens on a commercial scale are fundamentally the same, but the manipulative practices and equipment differ. Each must select breeder queens, obtain and prepare larvae for development into queens, prepare cell-building colonies to provide the proper environment for the developing larvae, and provide nuclei sufficiently large to care for the queen while she matures sexually, mates, and begins to lay.

Selection of Breeder Queens

The selection of breeding queens is the first important step in queen rearing. However competent the rearing methods, the resulting queens will be inferior if the stock is poor. Moreover, the selection of drone mothers is as important as the selection of queen mothers if the quality of the stock is to be maintained. (Selection of queens is discussed in detail in Chapter V.)

Producing Queens from Naturally Built Cells

SWARM CELLS

During the swarming season, many colonies in preparing to swarm build more cells than they will need to assure the survival of the colony. Cells of all ages are found in such colonies, a few cells being started each day for a period of several days. These cells vary in size and in the abundance of food they contain. The preconstructed cells are likely to be the largest, although cells built around very young larvae and well cared for may be just as large when finished. Some cells are small when sealed; these generally result from cells being constructed around older larvae which do not, while in the queen cell, have a feeding period long enough to produce a large queen.

Queen cells should be selected from the purely mated and high-producing colonies which have most of the characteristics one wishes to perpetuate. If the cells are built under desirable environmental conditions and are handled carefully, they should produce queens as good as those produced under natural conditions. The one undesirable factor is that by rearing queens only from colonies which swarm, one is likely to intensify the swarming trait in his colonies.

SUPERSEDURE CELLS

Most colonies will supersede their queens unless the beekeeper replaces the queens first. When queens are purely mated and their colonies have no strikingly bad traits, supersedure cells can be used to advantage instead of swarm cells. The removal of ripe supersedure cells frequently results in the colony building others, and this reaction may continue as long as the queen is able to lay and the colony is strong enough to build cells. If the colony is numerically strong to start with and the nectar and pollen conditions remain favorable, ripe queen cells can be removed every few days. However, since supersedure cells are built when the queen is failing, and since this may occur in early spring, midsummer, or late fall, this method of securing cells is not dependable, for it lends itself to the production of only a few queens at uncertain times of the year. It should be remembered that the uncritical use of supersedure cells is subject to the same dangers inherent in the use of swarm cells.

CELLS PRODUCED UNDER QUEENLESS OR EMERGENCY CONDITIONS

Colonies will produce queen cells when the bees and young brood are separated from their queen. This reaction may occur under a number of circumstances, among which the most important are:

1. when the queen is killed or removed from the hive;
2. when the brood nest is divided by means of a queen excluder and the queenless division has young brood, a situation which frequently occurs when a colony is "Demareed" for swarm control;
3. when a colony is divided and the queenless portion is placed in a separate location;
4. when bees are shaken into a hive, nucleus, or ventilated box without a queen, are given combs of pollen, and honey, or sugar syrup, and are supplied with young brood.

The queen breeder may take advantage of this replacement tendency, manipulating these conditions to get a colony to build as many cells as he desires. But in each case conditions favorable to the production of good queen cells must be present.

One of the earliest methods of producing queens was simply to remove the queen from a populous colony when nectar and pollen were plentiful and then, ten to eleven days later, to cut the mature queen cells from the combs and transfer them to queen mating hives. This method was improved later by removing all unsealed brood from such a colony and giving it a comb containing eggs and young larvae from a more desirable strain. If the colony has access to combs of pollen and is fed sugar syrup while the cells are being built, the colony will rear a number of cells.

If a colony is starting to build queen cell cups and is making other preparations to swarm, it will continue to do so if the queen is confined to the brood chamber and most of the combs of brood are placed above the queen excluder. Queen cells will be started, typically, in the queenless portion, particularly if the colony is strong enough to occupy three stories and the brood is placed in the top one. The condition of the colony can be improved for cell building by the addition of more bees from other colonies or by the addition of emerging brood and bees. Continuous feeding of sugar syrup or dilute honey is essential to assure optimum conditions for the production of the queen cells. Since the colony is queenright, it is quite likely to start swarm cells in the lower chambers as well as above, and those in the lower chamber must be torn down every week in order to prevent the colony from swarming. One can avoid the necessity of examining the lower chamber for swarm cells by removing the queen entirely and adding emerging brood or young bees from other colonies to maintain its strength. It is a good practice also to clip the queen's wings so that, if the bees do swarm, they will return to the hive.

A colony in this condition will continue to rear good queen cells as long as the queenless portion is supplied every three or four days with young larvae. Unless she reduces her brood rearing under the swarming impulse, the queen below will maintain the strength of the colony. In order to assure an adequate number of nurse bees in the queen cell compartment, it is desirable to move up combs containing young larvae from the lower brood chamber every time it is examined for queen cells. This should be done at intervals of no longer than seven days.

One disadvantage of permitting the bees to select their own larvae from which to produce cells is that they choose some larvae which are too old to produce the best queens. This is not an uncommon occurrence when colonies are made queenless or are divided, and are then left to rear their own queen under less than ideal conditions. This disadvantage can be overcome by supplying the queenless portion with a comb containing only eggs or hatching larvae taken from a choice colony. Another disadvantage is that the queen cells have to be cut from the comb, a task which is rather messy and results in injury to the comb. The Miller method of producing queen cells avoids some of these problems.

One can avoid the necessity of examining the lower chamber for swarm cells by removing the queen entirely and adding emerging brood or young bees from other colonies to maintain its strength.

Producing Queens under Controlled Conditions

OBTAINING AND PREPARING LARVAE FOR THE CELL BUILDERS

After the breeding queens have been selected, the next step is to obtain larvae from them and prepare the larvae for the cell builders. The way this is done will be governed by whether the larvae are to remain in the cells in which they hatched or to be transferred to queen cell cups for the remainder of their growth and development. The beekeeper with few colonies and a need for few queens may prefer not to transfer the larvae.

The Miller Method. The method popularized by Dr. C. C. Miller[1] is the simplest of all the procedures and is probably the best for the amateur beekeeper to use. Two or more strips of foundation two or three inches wide at the top and tapering to a point to within an inch or two of the bottom bar are fastened to the top bar of an empty frame (Fig. 14). The frame is then put into a breeder colony. Although the bees are bringing in nectar, the colony should be fed. To prevent the bees from building drone cells, combs of honey or sealed brood are substituted for all but two frames of brood between which the prepared frames are placed. In about a week the bees will have drawn out the foundation and the comb will contain brood, with the youngest brood and eggs toward the edges.

---

[1] Miller, C. C. 1912. How best queen cells can be secured. Amer. Bee Jour. 52(8):243.

Since the combs built from these foundation strips are not wired into the frame and since they are constructed of new white wax, they fall out of the frames easily if they are shaken or if the frame is turned on its side. They must be handled carefully. When the comb is removed from the breeder colony, the bees should be brushed off gently and the comb laid flat on a table or board for trimming. The egg-containing outer margins of the comb are trimmed away with a warm, sharp knife, leaving the youngest larvae in worker cells at the new comb margins. The comb is now ready to be put into a queenless cell-building colony. Combs containing larvae to be used for cell building, and the queen cells themselves should *never* be shaken. The bees should always be brushed off.

The Alley Method. The method developed by Henry Alley[2] resembles Miller's in that the larvae are allowed to remain in the cells of the worker comb in which they hatched. In Alley's method, an empty comb is placed into the brood nest of a breeder colony; four days later it usually contains eggs and newly hatched larvae. The comb is then cut from the frame with a warm, sharp knife, and into strips by running the knife through the middle of alternate rows of cells, leaving a center row intact. With the warm knife, the cell walls of one side of the comb are shaved down to within one-fourth inch of the midrib

Fig. 14. Frame prepared with strips of foundation for use with the Miller method.

[2] Alley, Henry. 1883. The beekeepers handy book, or twenty-two years experience in queen rearing. 184 pp.

and every second and third larva in the row of intact cells is destroyed. These strips are attached to a dark comb from which the lower two-thirds has been cut out and removed. The strip is fastened by dipping its uncut cells into melted beeswax and rosin just at its melting point, and by pressing it against the lower edge of the comb and holding it there until the wax had cooled somewhat. The cells containing the larvae are thus situated so they open downward. As soon as the strip is fastened to the comb, the frame is placed in the cell builder.

The Smith Method. In a modification of the Alley Method which Jay Smith adapted to large-scale queen production,[3] only new combs are used as the bees find them easier than older comb to remodel into queen cells. Each breeder queen is housed in a specially modified hive body which has a partition dividing it into a small compartment capable of taking three standard frames and a large compartment capable of holding six frames. The partition extends to within an inch of the bottom board; the remaining space is filled with a strip of queen excluder. In Smith's hive, the partition extends three-quarter inch above the top of the hive and each compartment is closed on top with a wooden inner cover. A telescope cover fits over all. A modification, whereby the partition is flush with the top of the hive and water-resistant canvas covering the frames of each compartment is attached to the upper edge of the partition, is equally effective and is easier to work with. In both types, the small compartment has no entrance and the entrance to the large compartment is located halfway up the side, just beneath the handhold and of similar dimensions. A hole bored in the hive wall provides access to a feeder attached to the outer wall of the small compartment.

The queen is confined to the small compartment on three frames. Two of these, which remain against each side wall, have a piece of comb nine and one-half inches long by five and one-half inches wide attached to the top bar at the middle; the remainder of the frame is filled with wood (Fig. 15). The third frame contains a piece of white comb of similar size. This frame is placed between the two side frames. The restricted comb area in the small compartment will cause the queen to lay promptly in the white comb, which can then be cut into strips and attached to bars.

The white comb is obtained by fastening a piece of foundation, nine and one-half by five and one-half inches, to the top bar of an empty

[3] Smith, Jay. 1949. Better Queens. 100 pp. Printed by Jay Smith.

Fig. 15. Smith "wooden frame" for use in breeder hive.

frame and then putting the prepared frame above an excluder in a strong colony or in the larger compartment of the breeder hive. When the cells are partly drawn the comb is ready for the breeder queen.

To make up the breeder colony, the breeding queen and one frame of brood are put into the small compartment, with the frame of brood between the frames containing the small combs. The remaining brood and bees are put into the larger compartment. The colony is fed; feeding must be continuous as long as cells are being raised. After the queen has filled the small side combs with brood, the center brood comb is removed and one of the new combs is put in its place. Twenty-four hours later, the new comb should be well filled with eggs. It is then placed in either the large compartment of the breeder hive or in a cell finisher for incubation and for the first feeding of the larvae. This sequence is repeated daily as long as larvae are needed. By the time the fourth comb of eggs is ready for incubation, the first should have abundantly-fed larvae and be ready to prepare for the cell builder.

The breeder colony cannot maintain itself when the young brood is repeatedly removed, and combs of emerging brood should be given at least once a week. Smith opens the starter colony in front of the breeder hive when the cells are removed from the starter. Many of the younger bees then join the breeder colony. Bees from one comb of the starter may also be shaken into the breeder colony as needed.

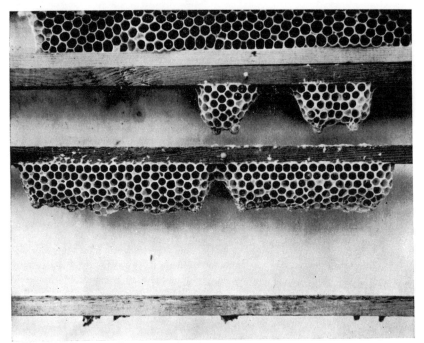

Fig. 16. Queen cells produced by the Smith method are usually webbed together.

In preparing the larvae for the cell builders, the comb containing the day-old larvae is cut from the frame and into strips as in the Alley method. Then, using a small paint brush, melted wax is painted on one side of a bar and a strip of cells is pressed onto the wax. Wax is then painted on both sides of the cell strip to attach it more firmly to the bar. The bar with the attached strip is dipped for a moment into cold water barely covering the painted wax, and the painting-dipping process is repeated until a heavy base is made.

At this point, the worker cells are too close together to permit the construction of queen cells from each one, so only every third larva is left, the two between being destroyed. Two bars of the prepared cells are put into a frame and two such frames are put into a starter colony. Smith used a "swarm box" to get the cells started.

The danger of overheating the larvae in the cells when the pieces of comb are fastened to the cell bars with melted beeswax can be avoided by using a split cell bar and fastening the strip to it by squeezing the cell walls opposite the prepared side between the two pieces of the bar. Additional support can be secured by using small brads in one piece of the bar and pushing them into the other half. If the cell bars have been coated with wax before they are pressed tightly together with the strip of comb in between, the extended cells will support the weight of the bees until the cell builders can further fasten the strip in place. This technique speeds up the operation and reduces the hazard of injuring the young larvae through exposure to drying or to unfavorable temperatures. But unless the pieces of comb are held securely in place the bees will pull them down or cut them away from the bar.

The Doolittle or Grafting Method. The essential feature of the Doolittle method of producing queen cells is the transference of young worker larvae to prepared queen cell cups. The larvae are taken from brood combs previously placed in breeder colonies. In this method of preparing larvae for the cell builders, the kind of comb used is unimportant as long as it is worker comb. The care of the larvae before they are transferred is just as important, however, as the care of the larvae prepared by the above methods for the cell builders. The larvae are transferred to queen cell cups when they are 12 to 24 hours old,

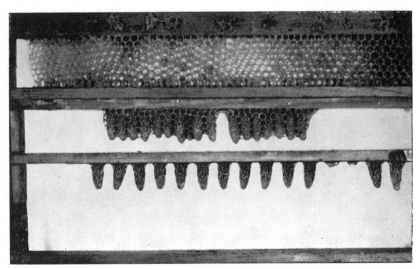

Fig. 17. Queen cells produced by the Smith method (upper bar) and by the Doolittle method (lower bar).

and it is important that they be well fed from the time of hatching until they are used.

Preparing Larvae by the Doolittle Method

Obtaining Larvae

To obtain larvae for grafting, a dark comb, preferably one which has been polished and conditioned above the brood nest of a populous colony, is put into the brood nest of a breeder colony. The next day the comb is put into an incubator colony, and three days later the oldest larvae should be about 24 hours old and ready for grafting. The sequence should be initiated daily so that there will be a regular sup-

Fig. 18. A special hive to procure young larvae for grafting. The queen is confined on small combs in the compartment enclosed with queen-excluding zinc and combs are exchanged in rotation with the other half of the center compartment. One center device is in place in the hive and a second one is included above the hive to reveal the details of construction. The hive is covered when in use with a burlap beneath the outer cover.

ply of larvae of the right age for grafting. The transfer to an incubator colony is important because larvae left in the regular breeder colony from hatching to grafting tend to receive less than ideal care.

Larvae cared for in incubator colonies from hatching to grafting should be as adequately fed as larvae of comparable age prepared by the Miller or Alley methods. If the bed of jelly is transferred to the cell cups with the larva, the period of short food supply, if it occurs at all, should be reduced to a matter of minutes. In order to make certain that the queen will lay a desired number of eggs in the comb provided, the brood chambers can be divided into three parts, of three combs each, by means of queen excluders. The queen is confined to the central division, whose two outer combs should be filled with brood, pollen, and honey. The two side divisions can be stocked with emerging brood to keep up the strength of the colony. The comb to be placed in the center can often be taken from one of the side divisions.

THE QUEEN CELL CUPS

Queen cell cups to receive the larvae may be obtained by the amateur beekeeper in several ways. When few queens are needed, a sufficient supply of cups can be obtained by cutting off the "embryo" cups which are present in most colonies. Doolittle followed this practice before he began making cups by dipping. Strips of drone comb which have been shaved down to within one-quarter inch of the midrib and in which every third cell has been mashed down make good cups. Pressed wax cups can be purchased from supply dealers at a reasonable cost. Or the beekeeper can make his own cups by dripping or by other methods (Fig. 19).

Dipping Single Cell Cups. The small beekeeper usually finds a single forming stick (Fig. 20) adequate for dipping cells. The stick, made of round hardwood about three inches long, has a three-eighth-inch diameter at a point one-half inch from the tip, tapering to between one-quarter and five-sixteenths of an inch at the tip. The end is rounded, to give the bottom of the wax cell a concave form. The forming stick can be made by the beekeeper or purchased from supply dealers. It can be tested for size by fitting the end into a naturally built queen cell cup.

The wax to be used in making cell cups should be clean. New, light

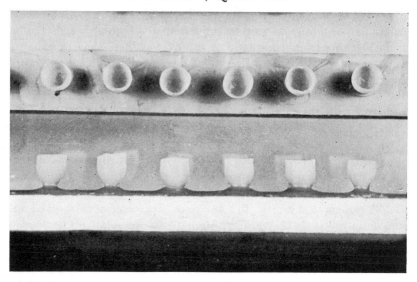

Fig. 19. Wax cell cups for use with the Doolittle method.

wax is preferable, but darker wax is satisfactory. The wax can be melted in a water-jacketed tray and should be kept at a temperature just above its melting point.

When the wax is ready, the forming stick is dipped into cold water, the excess water is shaken off, and the stick is dipped into the wax to a depth of about three-eighths of an inch. The stick is quickly re-

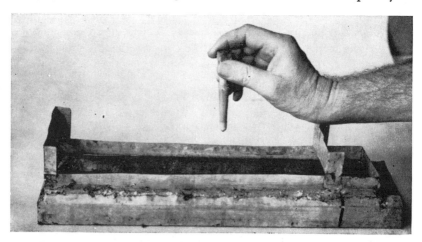

Fig. 20. Dipping cells with a single forming stick.

moved and held in the air until the wax has solidified, then again dipped into the wax and quickly removed. This process is repeated four or five times. After the final dipping, the mold is immersed into the cold water and left there a few moments. A gentle twist will then remove the cell cup from the stick. The stick must be dipped in water again before the next cell is formed.

The prepared wax cups must now be attached to bars just long enough to fit between the end bars of a standard frame. The bars can be made from regular frame bottom bars. The frame to receive the bars should preferably be no wider than the cell bars. It should have blocks one-quarter inch thick, three-quarters wide and one and one-half inches long nailed to the inside of the end bars to form ledges on which the cell bars can rest. The lower blocks should touch the bottom bar. The lower ends of the second pair of blocks should be spaced about three-eighths inch above the tops of the first blocks, and the lower end of the third pair of blocks should be the same distance above the upper ends of the second pair. A frame so prepared will take three bars of cells and have about a two-inch space for comb beneath the top bar. A strip of tin can be tacked on one side of the end bars to keep the cell bars from falling out.

In attaching cell cups to the bars, some melted wax is poured along one side of the bar to form a base for the cells. Each wax cup is picked up by inserting the forming stick into it. The end of the cup is dipped into the melted wax, and the cup bottom is then lightly pressed into the wax on the bar. The cups are spaced about three-quarters to seven-eighths inch from center to center; 15 or 16 cups are placed on each bar. When a bar is filled, melted wax is poured along each side of and between the cell cups, reinforcing their attachment to the bar and making a firm base by which to handle the cells when the bees have completed them.

Quantity Production. When cell cups are needed in large quantities, dipping one cup at a time is impractical. A form for dipping many cups at once can be made by attaching a number of cell forming sticks to a wooden block or a strip of wood. A convenient form has a row of 15 or 16 forming sticks spaced three-quarters inch apart from center to center. The sticks are all the same length. They must be kept clean and polished. They can be cleaned by boiling in water for a few minutes, and may be polished with a soft cloth. The form should be soaked in cold water for half an hour just before it is to be used.

Fig. 21. The Rauchfuss cell-dipping machine. The block-tin molds are first run through a thin cool starch or soap solution and then through melted beeswax. (This machine is no longer available.)

Pure, clean beeswax should be used for making the cell cups. It should be melted in a water-jacketed tray long enough to permit the entire row of forming sticks to be dipped at once. The tray should have adjustable guides for gauging the depth to which the cells are dipped. The temperature of the wax should be maintained at just above its melting point. A second supply of melted wax for attaching the cups to the bars is also needed; wax from the dipping tray should not be used for this purpose lest its wax level drop too rapidly. A tray containing cold water, also long enough to receive the entire row of forming sticks, is also required. This water dip should contain a small amount of soap or cool, thin starch solution. A large container of cold water should be available for cooling and washing the cell cups.

To make the cups, the pre-soaked sticks are first dipped in the soapy solution, then shaken or touched to a towel to remove excess water. They are then dipped about three-eighths inch into the melted wax

Fig. 22. Dipping many cells at once.

in the tray and then immediately withdrawn and held above the tray until the wax on the sticks has cooled somewhat and solidified (Fig. 22). This dipping process is repeated four or five times.

After the last dip, bases of the wax cups are rested on a bar over the second tray of beeswax, the form being steadied with one hand or by other support. Melted wax is ladled over the upper surface of the bar along each side of the cells and between the bases of the wax cups (Fig. 23). With the forming sticks still steadied against the bar, both

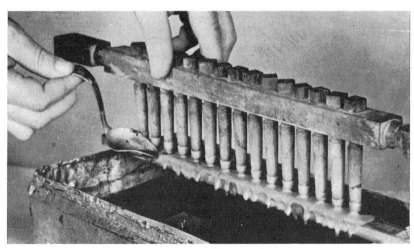

Fig. 23. Attaching the cups to the bar with melted wax.

Fig. 24. Removing forming sticks from the cell cups after first being dipped in cold water.

are lifted from the ladling tray and lowered into the tray of cold water for a few moments. While the cups are held under water the forming sticks are retracted from them by evenly pushing the cell bar away from the forming sticks as illustrated in Fig. 24.

Some queen breeders arrange the cells in two rows on a wider bar, so the cells can be concentrated nearer the center of the brood chamber. The use of a single row of cells on a bar only slightly wider than the width of the finished cells is most common, however.

GRAFTING AND TRANSFERRING LARVAE TO QUEEN-CELL CUPS

Careful attention to the temperature, light, and humidity of the room in which the grafting is done is particularly important if a large number of cells are needed. The temperature should be at least 75°F; humidity around 50 per cent is necessary to prevent dehydration of larvae or royal jelly used to prime the cells. Humidification can be provided by a pan of water on a stove, by sprinkling the floor with water, or by hanging wet cloths in the room. Damp cloths laid over the grafted cells will aid in preventing the drying of the brood food and larvae even if the humidity of the room is low.

Good light is essential. It should be bright enough and so located that the larvae can be picked up and transferred quickly and without injury. Sunlight can be used, but care must be taken to prevent its heat from injuring the larvae. A fluorescent lamp makes one of the most satisfactory lights for all weather conditions.

The proper conditions of warmth, humidity, and light can best be provided by a small grafting house located near the cell builders. It need not be large, but should have space enough for a work bench and stool, storage for cell bars and frames to hold them, and a wall area for a record and work chart showing the origin of the larvae and the disposition of the cells, as well as have a dependable source of heat and light. The combs of larvae and the grafted cells should be protected by carrying them in a covered comb carrier or box between the colonies and the grafting place.

Two types of transferring or grafting needles are in use, the straight and the automatic (Fig. 25). The former may be constructed from a six-inch piece of 14-gauge wire (about the size of baling wire). One end is flattened and expanded, the tip rounded and bent at about a 30° angle one-quarter to one-half inch from the end. This is the "jelly spoon." The other end is flattened and tapered to about one-thirty-seconds inch, with the point made very thin. The terminal one-six-teenths inch is bent at about an 80° angle to form the lifting hook. The underside of this hook should be rounded so that the hook does not dig into the cell bottom when it is slipped under the larva. The terminal one-half inch is also bent at a 30° angle to give unobstructed vision into the cell.

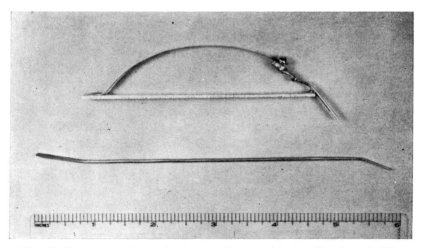

Fig. 25. Two types of transferring needles: straight needle (lower); Pierce or Macy automatic needle (upper).

The other type of needle, known as the Pierce or Macy Automatic Needle, is shaped like a bow. An extension at one end is inserted into the cell. Depressing the curved part of the bow ejects a piece of watch spring from within the extension, and this slips under the larva. Releasing the pressure on the bow causes the spring to retract into the extension, leaving the larva at the latter's end. The springs sold with these tools have sharp corners which tend to dig into the cell bottom; these corners must be rounded before the needle works satisfactorily. Using a sideways movement in slipping the extended tip under the larvae also reduces the risk of damage.

If the straight needle is used the cells should be "primed" with jelly. This facilitates the removal of the larva from the needle tip, furnishes food for the larva, and prevents its drying. For the first graft, a bar of queen cells may be grafted "dry" (without jelly). Jelly can be obtained from natural cells or from previously grafted cells which have not been sealed. The larva should be removed from the cell and the jelly diluted with an equal volume of *warm* water; the mixture should be stirred until it has an even consistency. A portion of the diluted jelly is then taken up with a jelly spoon, from which an amount about the size of a large pin head, or a No. 4 shot is scraped off and deposited in the center of the bottom of each wax cup (Fig. 26), or the jelly can be put into the cups with a medicine dropper. When the automatic needle is used, the cups need not be primed, for

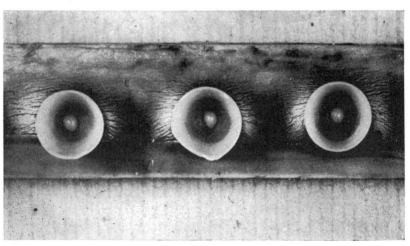

Fig. 26. Cell cups "primed" with royal jelly.

this needle picks up considerable jelly with the larva, and the jelly and larva are deposited together in the bottom of the cell cup. Larvae can be transferred to dry cups most successfully if the larvae are taken from well-provisioned cells.

When daylight is used as a source of light, the operator should seat himself and adjust the position of the comb until the larvae can be seen easily. With the bar of cell cups resting on the comb, the point of the straight grafting needle is carefully inserted in the royal jelly beneath the larva by sliding the needle down the side of the cell wall and slipping the point sideways under the larva. The larva is then lifted out of the cell and transferred to the top of the jelly in the cell cup. The larva is actually floated off the needle and is not immersed in the jelly. If the automatic needle is used, the extension is lowered along a side of a cell to the bottom, and then the bow is depressed so that the spring, protruding from the end, can be slipped under the larva and its bed of jelly. With the bow still depressed, the larva is lifted from the cell and lowered to the bottom of a cell cup. Release of the pressure allows the spring to withdraw, leaving the larva on a bed of jelly on the cup bottom. When larvae are transferred dry with a straight needle, the hook of the needle is pressed lightly into the cell bottom, permitting the larva to be deposited on its own bed of jelly.

When artificial light is used, the comb may be laid on a table with the top bar toward the operator and with the bottom bar elevated about two inches. The light should then be over the comb or above the operator. When the frame is thus situated, the bar of cups can be laid on the comb just above the area furnishing the larvae (Fig. 27).

If the process of transferring the larvae is slow, each bar should be put into the cell builder as soon as grafted. If the process is rapid, three or more bars may be grafted before they are put in the cell builder. Care should be taken, as previously noted, to keep the larvae from becoming chilled or dry during the transferring process. The quicker the larvae receive the care of the nurse bees the less likely they are to be injured.

DOUBLE GRAFTING

Double grafting is the removal of the larvae from accepted cells one or two days after grafting and replacing them with larvae 24 hours old. This, theoretically at least, provides the larvae with abundant food from the time of transfer and generally insures that considerably

Fig. 27. Transferring larvae into cell cups.

more food is put into the queen cells than the larvae can eat. The replacement larvae should be fed in an incubator colony from hatching, and should always be liberally supplied with jelly. Larvae scantily fed before transfer are not likely to make good queens regardless of the way they are grafted. The possibility of neglect and inadequate feeding during the short period immediately following grafting is relatively minor compared with the possibility of skimpy feeding during the longer period prior to grafting. The essential point is that the larvae be provided with an abundance of suitable food from the moment of hatching until the period of feeding is finished.

When cells are double grafted, care should be exercised in the second transfer. Unless the larvae are removed without materially changing the consistency of the royal jelly, the bees may remove all of the jelly and start over again, thus eliminating any beneficial effect the double graft might possibly have.

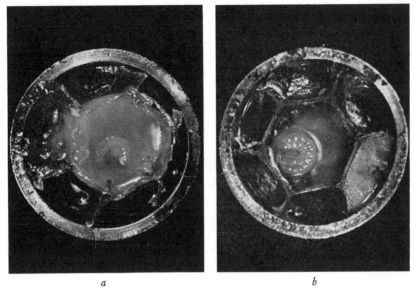

a   b

Fig. 28. *a*, A well-fed 36-hour-old larva. This is the oldest larva which should be grafted. *b*, A 48-hour-old larva. This size larva is difficult to transfer.

The Cell Builders

Cell builders may be either queenless or queenright. Either type must include abundant bees of all ages and be especially strong in nurse bees. Each must be well provisioned with honey and pollen and fed stimulatively. The nurse bees must be concentrated in the cell-building area.

A special candy is excellent for stimulative feeding. The ingredients are:

> 200 pounds of granulated sugar (beet or cane)
> 10 pounds of honey
> 60 cups of soybean flour
> 10 cups of brewers' yeast
> 10 cups of powdered skim milk
> 1½ cups of vinegar
> 5 gallons of water
> 60 grams of sodium sulfathiazole (2 ounces
>   plus 2 teaspoons)

The water, vinegar, and honey are heated in a water-jacketed tank. The sodium sulfathiazole is added, and the mixture is stirred until all components are in solution. Sugar, soybean flour, yeast, and powdered skim milk are mixed separately, then added slowly to the warm solution with constant stirring. (Premixing of the dry ingredients helps avoid "lumping.") Heating and stirring continue until a temperature of approximately 200°F is reached. The mixture is then ready to be poured into molds. Many beekeepers use candy boards made of masonite with a one-inch-deep rim of the same dimensions as the top of the hive body and having the rough part of the masonite inside the rim. When cold, the candy is sufficiently firm to remain in the boards, which are then inverted over the top bars beneath the outer cover. The above mixture makes approximately 30 boards. The candy can also be molded in blocks that can be tied into frames and then hung in the hive in place of a comb.

Some beekeepers use 60 teaspoons of TM-25 (approximately 6½ ounces) instead of the sodium sulfathiazole when they wish to prevent EFB as well as AFB. Although it is known that heat tends to destroy the effectiveness of terramycin, there does not seem to be any experimental evidence regarding its effectiveness on EFB when used in this cooked candy.

Larvae prepared by the Miller or Alley methods will be accepted most successfully in queenless hives or in the swarm box, while grafted cells will be accepted by either queenless or queenright cell builders or in the swarm box.

THE QUEENRIGHT CELL BUILDER

Queenright cell builders are used extensively for finishing cells started in swarm boxes or starter hives. They are used by some commercial operators both to start and to finish cells.

Queenright cell builders must be as strong as queenless ones. This makes swarming somewhat a problem but the difficulty can be overcome by using young clipped queens, by removing natural cells, and by replacing young brood in the brood nest with emerging brood or empty combs at least once, and preferably twice, a week. Queenright cell builders may be either two- or three-story colonies.

The two-story queenright cell builder is suitable for commercial

Fig. 29. Two-story cell builders.

queen-rearing operations and is also recommended when only a few cells are to be produced by the grafting method. Colonies selected for cell builders should be strong, or emerging brood and bees should be added to bring them to the desired strength. The colonies should completely fill the two bodies, and should be fed for at least three days prior to use as cell builders. The cell builders should be made up one day before giving them the first lot of cells. The queen should be clipped in order to prevent loss of the bees if the colony should swarm.

In making up the two-story cell builder, the queen is left in the lower body with emerging and sealed brood and often with an empty comb. All unsealed brood is put into the second body to bring the nurse bees to the cell-building area. A comb of honey and pollen is placed next to the two side walls of the upper body and the unsealed brood is put toward the center with the youngest in the middle, where the first cells will be put later. A frame containing pollen is also placed near the middle so it will be readily available to the nurses. Remaining spaces, if any, are filled with emerging brood from other colonies. This body is then placed upon the lower body, and separated from it by an excluder. The cell-building colony of bees should be fed *continuously*.

A few hours prior to giving the first cells to the cell builder, the frame of larvae at the center is removed, leaving a frame of young larvae on one side of the space and the pollen comb on the other. The nurse bees, which had been feeding the larvae which were removed, cluster in this space and are eager to feed the cells given to them. Thereafter new cells are given every third or fourth day.

The arrangement of placing newly grafted cells between a frame with young larvae and a frame with pollen should be maintained. By the time each new graft is given to the cell builder, the cells of the preceding graft should be at the sealing stage, no longer requiring the attention of nurse bees. After the cells are sealed they are merely incubated by the cell-building colony, and their location in the hive is not important as long as proper temperature is maintained. It is advantageous, however, to establish a definite routine so that cells of different ages are located in a specific relation to each other. Such a system eliminates searching for the oldest cells and guards against leaving ripe cells to emerge in the cell builder.

One such system is simply to place the new graft between a frame of young larvae and a pollen comb in the same part of the hive, pushing the older cells to one side. As more frames of cells are added, combs of honey or brood must be removed to make room for the new cells. Eventually three or four frames of cells of different ages coexist in the cell builder in a frame arrangement of *b-c-c-c-L-C-P-l-h* (b = sealed or emerging brood; c = older cells; L = young larvae; C = new cells; P = pollen comb; l = older larvae; and h = honey).

When a three-day interval of grafting is used, there is considerable merit in removing the nine-day-old queen cells at the time the third graft is given. The frames of cells can be placed in an incubator and prepared for the nuclei the following morning without again disturbing the cell builder. The incubator temperature should be kept at 93°F and the humidity around 50 per cent. Great care in maintaining a suitable temperature for the developing queens is critical at this time. Any sudden or prolonged chilling will tend to retard the growth of the queen and could result in underdeveloped wings.

Maintainance of Queenright Cell Builders. The queens in queenright cell builders usually maintain a good egg-laying rate and thus keep the colony strong. If more bees or brood are needed, they should be supplied from other colonies. The brood emerging below gives room for the queen to lay, and the young bees are attracted to the body above by the larvae there. Not all the eggs and larvae can be put above, however, and about four days after the colony is rearranged new larvae are hatching in quantity below the excluder and more nurse bees are required in the lower body. The larvae which were put above are mostly sealed by this time, so fewer nurse bees are required to care for the young larvae which were raised above the excluder. Thus there tends to be a reversal of nurse bee concentration. It then becomes necessary to raise combs of unsealed brood from below, exchanging them for combs of emerging brood or of honey above, putting the youngest larvae next to the youngest cells in the center of the second body. This exchange in the position of the larvae and emerging or sealed brood should be made every three or four days. It is good practice to make the exchange each time a graft is given.

Many queen breeders prefer to give their cell-building colonies two or three bars of cells every fourth instead of every third day, as just described. In this program, the cells are generally ready to be sealed shortly after the next lot is added and are simply pushed toward the opposite side of the hive, with a frame of young brood placed between the last frame of cells and the one newly supplied. Ten days after the first graft is given to the cell builder, the first frame of cells has to be removed. It is desirable at this time also to check the condition of the colony below the queen excluder for queen cells, and to raise brood, add bees, or otherwise bring the colony up to its peak of queen-rearing efficiency if such changes are needed.

The three-story queenright cell builder is made up and maintained in the same way as the two-story arrangement, but with a super of combs placed between the lower body with the queen and the upper body with the cells. An excluder separates the bottom body from the two upper chambers. During the early spring and periods of dearth this super should be well filled with honey and pollen, but during a good flow the full super should be replaced with a super of empty combs in which the strong colony can store honey. It may be necessary to make this exchange several times if the flow is heavy. The three-story cell builder requires more bees than the two-story unit to fill the entire hive. There is no particular advantage in using a three-story cell builder at the beginning of operations, but as the honey flow increases a super may become a necessity.

In some cases, the queen cells are placed in the second story of a

Fig. 30. Three-story queenright cell builder showing colony strength necessary for the production of good cells.

three-story queenright (or queenless) cell builder, on the theory that the super of honey and bees above tends to stabilize the temperatures during spring or early summer.

A three-story cell builder may be strengthened by adding one or two hive bodies of emerging brood, bees, and pollen from other colonies. The lower hive body is used to produce the comb of larvae which is placed next to the frame of newly grafted cells. Two or three pounds of young bees are sometimes added at weekly or ten-day intervals to insure the presence of an abundance of nurse bees at all times. The greatest problem with strong three-story queenright cell builders is to prevent them from swarming.

THE QUEENLESS CELL BUILDER

Queenless cell builders may be used to start and complete cells, or to finish cells started in swarm boxes or starting colonies. These colonies, which cannot maintain themselves, need supporting colonies for a brood supply. Queenless cell builders may be of one, two, or three stories.

Before the queenless cell builders are made up, the bees should be fed honey or sugar syrup for at least a day or two. Pollen should be added if an insufficient amount is available in the field. The pollen may be fed in cakes, in candy, in sugar syrup, in natural pollen combs, or by filling the cells of an empty comb about half full of pollen pellets and spraying the pellets with thin sugar syrup.

The one-story queenless cell builder is recommended when queen cells are produced by the Miller method. It is made up by dequeening the selected colony and leaving only sealed or emerging brood, except for two frames of very young larvae which are placed in the middle of the hive. A pollen comb is placed next to one of the combs of larvae. The outside combs should be well filled with pollen and honey. If necessary, more bees are added to make the colony very strong. The colony is fed for at least three days prior to dequeening and continuously thereafter unless a sufficient and reliable flow is on. The first cells may be given to the colony the day after it is made queenless.

Shortly before the first cells are given, the center comb of larvae is removed and the bees allowed to cluster in the space, which should now have a comb of pollen on one side and a comb of larvae on the other. Succeeding grafts, or prepared cells, are put in the center at three- or four-day intervals, the older ones being moved to the side as with queenright cell builders.

Queenless cell builders are maintained by replacing combs from which bees have emerged with combs of sealed or emerging brood from the supporting colonies. This is done once a week. The comb of larvae should be replaced with younger larvae a few hours prior to each graft, and the other cells should be shifted to their new location in the hive. The "ripe" cells are also removed the ninth or tenth day after grafting. Occasionally it may be necessary to add more bees. The additional bees, from an outyard if possible, should be shaken into a screened cage and supplied with sugar syrup. Several hours or a day later, they are sprayed lightly with sugar syrup just before they are added to the cell builder.

The first body of the two-story queenless cell builder should be well filled with honey and pollen, and the second body should be made up and maintained as above. Nearly twice as many bees are required to fill the hive as is required for the one-story cell builder.

The first body of the three-story queenless cell builder should be well filled with sealed brood and pollen and the third body with sealed brood and honey. The middle body is made up and maintained like the one-story cell builder. All three bodies must be filled with bees.

Cell builders will often build natural cells. All of the brood combs should be examined once a week and the queen cells destroyed. Enough bees should be shaken from each comb to expose cells which may be hidden in the comb corners.

As a means of saving labor, a California beekeeper who uses the three-story queenless cell builder hinges the second and third stories together at the back and simply leans the top story back on a stake, driven to the height of the second story, when he operates the frames of cells in the second story (Fig. 31). In order to save time and to prevent the possibility of overlooking a natural queen cell, he does

Fig. 31. Three-story queenless cell builders with the top body hinged to the middle body to facilitate manipulations.

not add unsealed brood after the cell builders are made up initially. His experience indicates that good cells can be produced in strong, queenless and broodless colonies if new grafts are given every third day and two to three pounds of young bees are added every week to ten days.

Sometimes a swarm will enter a cell builder, or a virgin may enter and be accepted by the bees. The cells will then be torn down by the bees. This can be prevented by placing an excluder between the bottom board and the body of a one-story queenless cell builder, or between the first and second bodies of two- or three-story units.

Overheating should be avoided in all cell-building colonies. When colonies are placed in the sun without shade boards, insulated tops, or adequate ventilation, the temperature of the upper part of the hive may rise so high at times that many of the bees may leave, crowding into the lower hive region or hanging onto the outside. The cells will be neglected to a greater or less extent and poor queens may result, despite a sufficiency of bees and otherwise excellent conditions.

During periods of heavy honey flow, the bees often build comb on the sealed queen cells, particularly if they are made by the Alley method. This can be prevented to some extent by putting a frame or two of foundation in the cell builder or by using narrow frames for the cell bars. The narrow frames (as wide as a frame bottom bar) permit the bees to cluster on the cells when the adjacent frames are close to it, but do not provide space enough for the bees to build comb on the sides of the cells.

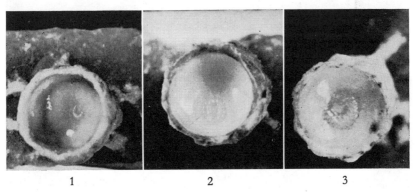

| 1 | 2 | 3 |

Fig. 32. Growth of larvae in queen cells one, two, and three days following grafting.

CELL-STARTER COLONIES

Queen cells can be started and finished in the same colony. Commercial queen breeders use this method extensively, although many prefer to start the cells in one colony and finish them in others. Either of two types of starting colonies may be used: the queenless starting colony, or the swarm box.

The queenless starting colony is made up from a colony, previously fed for three days, by removing the queen and all brood except two frames of larvae which are left at either side of the space for the center comb. A frame of pollen is put between them and the remainder of the body filled with combs of emerging brood. More bees are added if the colony does not completely cover all frames. The colony is fed again and is ready for cells about four or five hours later.

About an hour before the cells are to be given to the colony, the combs of larvae are removed. When the cells are grafted, they are put

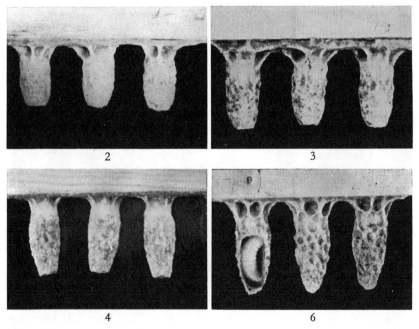

Fig. 33. Growth of queen cells. Cells shown at two, three, four, and six days following grafting.

in the places which were occupied by the frames of larvae. Two frames with grafted queen cell cups (90 to 120 cells) may be given at one time. They are removed 24 hours later and distributed to the finishing colonies, usually one to three bars of cells to each finisher.

This type of starter will start two to three successive grafts of cells, but as the bees grow older their efficiency as nurses decreases and fewer cells will be accepted and fed adequately. Thus starter colonies must be remade every two or three days, or new bees and brood must be added.

In Australia, some queen breeders who prefer to use a cell starter have a special hive with a lateral extension large enough to hold five combs. It is separated from the main hive by a wooden partition with a queen excluder at the bottom that can be closed with a sliding masonite strip. Young bees and brood are added from the supporting colony to give the desired strength of queenless bees several hours before the cells are given. Young bees from other colonies may be added as needed. Such colonies will start three bars of cells or will start and finish one bar of fifteen cells. In order to reduce robbing, they are fed at the back of the hive. If the queen excluder partition is not

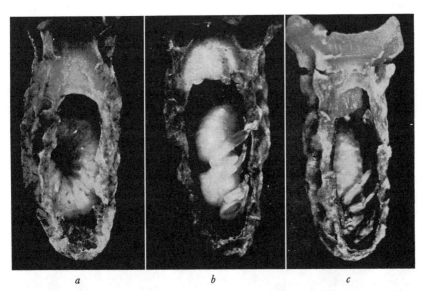

| a | b | c |

Fig. 34. Development of the queen. *a,* spinning stage; *b,* pupal stage; *c,* adult shortly prior to emergence. Note the surplus of royal jelly in the base of each cell.

covered when the cells are given to the cell-building unit, the entrance to the main colony is closed for 24 hours.

The swarm box type cell starter usually holds five standard frames, with a six-inch space below them screened on the sides. There is no entrance, and the bees are confined the entire time they are in the box. A comb of honey or sugar syrup is placed next to each wall and a comb of pollen is put in the center space. The box is now stocked with five to seven pounds of bees from the upper brood nest of a colony which, unless there was a good nectar flow, had been fed for three days previously. A feeder is put on the top and the box is set in a cool, dark place. Two to five hours later the bees are ready for cells. Some beekeepers fill the combs with sugar syrup or diluted honey rather than use a feeder.

Two frames with three or four bars each (about 90 to 120 cells) are given at one time. The box is jarred to knock the bees down and the frames with the cells are put into the two empty spaces. Twenty-four hours later the cells are removed and distributed to the finisher colonies. When the cells are removed, the swarm box is *not* jarred and the bees are brushed lightly from the cells. Queen cells should *never* be shaken.

Two or three succeeding grafts of cells can be started by the same lot of bees, after which they can be returned to the colony from which they came and the box restocked.

Another modification of the swarm-box type cell starter can be made by placing a hive body above a double-screen division board over the second story of a populous colony. It is filled with bees, combs of honey, pollen, and emerging brood from the lower colony and from a second supporting colony placed along side. A division-board feeder

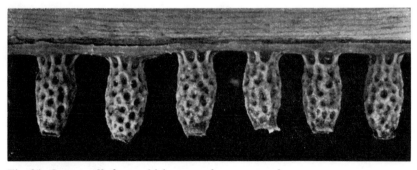

Fig. 35. Queen cells from which queens have emerged.

is used. The manipulation is made on the morning of the day the cells are to be grafted, and the grafting is done in late afternoon. A special cover can be used which does not have to be removed when the cells are inserted. Where the double-grafting technique is used, the cells are left with the starter colony for 24 hours and then are regrafted and distributed directly to the finishing colonies.

RECORDS

Simple records in a notebook, or on the hives, frames, or bars are sufficient when cells are raised in small numbers. When large numbers of cells are produced each day, a more complete automatic system is needed. The method of putting new cells in a definite place in the cell builder and moving the older ones to the side shows the relative ages of the different cells within the hive. If the cell builders are divided into three groups, each of which is lettered or numbered, and cells are put into a different group on successive days, a system of rotation is set up whereby each group of cell builders receives new cells and the ripe cells are removed every three days. All colonies of a particular group receive newly grafted cells the same day, and ripe cells are taken from them at the same time on the ninth day if they are placed in an incubator over night. Since any particular group will receive attention on different days of the week during successive weeks, records of each graft should be kept to show into which group of builders the cells were put and when they should come out. These records should also indicate the breeding queen used and into which nuclei or group of nuclei the cells were placed, if the queen breeder is to select stock for breeding purposes. The following type of record may be kept on a blackboard in the grafting house or on a sheet of paper:

Graft Record

Date Grafted	No. of Cells	Breeder	Cell Builder	No. Cells Accepted	Date Out	Dispo- sition of Cells	Remarks

Fig. 36. A frame of well-built queen cells.

The *date out* is entered at the time the graft is made. When cells are taken out of the builder, a line is drawn through the entry.

As many as three bars of cells (about 45 to 50 cells) can be put into a cell-building colony at one time, either for finishing or for both starting and finishing, and if it is in proper condition new cells can be given the cell builder every three days. Usually at least 75 per cent of the cells are accepted and satisfactorily completed. Thus each cell-building colony can be counted on to produce about 30 cells each three days, or at a rate of ten cells per day.

Many variations of these methods are in use. The feeding of the larvae is the important thing; when this is done properly, the system employed matters but little as long as it is economically sound and fits in with the beekeepers' operations.

A Bee House for Producing Queen Cells

Some commercial queen breeders erect substantial shelters in which to place their cell-building colonies as well as to provide a suitable place for preparing the larvae under all weather conditions. Frequently, such conveniences are provided in separate buildings or in rooms or addi-

Fig. 37. The "Long Idea" hive used by some beekeepers for cell building.

tions to warehouses where needed equipment is stored. A room ten feet wide and with two outside walls will provide adequate space for two rows of cell-building colonies and an ample aisle in between. For greater convenience in manipulation, the hives can be placed on benches. Windows can be arranged to permit exit for the bees which leave the hive when it is being manipulated. A work room for grafting or preparing the cells and larvae can be set up at one end. Heating units and a fan to distribute the heat evenly throughout the room may be desirable.

A California beekeeper has a bee house built onto the warehouse where he stores his nucleus boxes and other equipment (Fig. 38). This room, 8 by 60 feet, houses 19 specially made 15-frame hives used exclusively for cell building. The hive bodies are built to take the frames parallel to the outside hive entrance, which extends through the wall of the building. A division board permits expansion or contraction of the hive according to the strength of the colony or the number of frames used. Each hive is placed on a wall bracket at a convenient height. A built-in feeder delivers a constant supply of sugar syrup through a pipe line leading to all the hives from a vacuum tank at one end of the room.

Fig. 38. Interior of a bee house for producing queen cells.

An enlargement of the room at one end provides adequate space for the cell work. Good lighting at the work table and throughout the room makes it possible to graft at any time during the night or day, regardless of the weather. He is never troubled by wind or rain, light or darkness, and robbing is something he need not consider while working his cell builders. He can maintain whatever heat level he desires. The colonies themselves are heating units of no little value.

The adjacent warehouse is equally long but twice as wide. Here, in addition to storing nucleus boxes and other equipment and supplies, he makes up his baby nuclei to take the cells ten days after they were grafted. This room has a cooling system, for the nuclei are held in the warehouse from two to three days before transfer to their permanent locations.

The Routine Operation of a Bee House. A brief description of the management of cell-building colonies in this bee house reveals its utility in helping to produce a large number of cells with minimum labor. The cell-building colonies are established by setting into each 15-frame hive enough bees to crowd the hive. Combs of pollen saved from the previous season are added as needed. The colonies are kept queenless, but are given a frame of eggs or of newly hatching brood every third day. These combs are taken from supporting colonies located on the outside a few yards away. Additional bees are added, when necessary, to keep the cell builders filled.

The breeding queens are kept in divided hives with four combs in each division. In order to secure larvae of the proper age for grafting, black brood combs are placed in these divisions every third day and are used for grafting the larvae on the fourth day.

The cell-building colonies are divided into three groups. Each colony in a group receives three bars of sixteen cells every third day. The frame of grafted cells is placed near the center, in the same relative position in each hive, and the older cells and combs of older brood are moved toward the back of the hive. The date of the graft and the number of the queen from which the larvae were produced is noted on the top of the frame at the time it is grafted. Ten days after grafting, the ripe cells are removed, separated, and placed immediately in nuclei which had been made up in the nucleus room the day before.

While some queen breeders like to place grafted cells in their cell builders every fourth day, this beekeeper prefers to give his colonies cells every third day. He uses larvae which are generally between 24 and 40 hours old. These cells are sealed within a day after the new lot is given. Since the queen cells contain an excess of royal jelly and are large and well shaped, he reasons that they receive adequate food. The location of a comb of young unsealed brood on one side of the newly added frame of cells concentrates the nurse bees in that area.

The makeup of one of his cell builders after a new frame of cells has been given could be something like this: at the side of the hive next to the entrance through the wall is the feeder, then (1) a comb of honey and pollen, (2) honey and emerging brood, (3) brood (sealed), (4) pollen, (5) *new graft*, (6) hatching brood, (7) *queen cells three days old*, (8) older unsealed brood, (9) *queen cells six days old*, (10) sealed brood, (11) *queen cells nine days old*. The remaining frames are filled with brood and honey. Most available cells are filled with sugar syrup, honey, brood, or pollen, and the hive is so crowded with bees that many hang out on the side of the building near each entrance. The hives are closed with heavy canvas or a double thickness of burlap. The arrangement not only facilitates the entire cell-building operation but also reduces to a minimum the number of records which have to be kept.

The Care of Queen Cells

When ripe cells are removed, they are cut from the bars with a thin-bladed knife by stripping off the layer of wax fastening the cell cups to the bar. The cells are then separated. Small or poorly formed cells, which should be relatively few, are discarded. The cells are placed between layers of padded cloth and carried to the nucleus room or out to the mating yards.

Young queens emerge from their cells approximately thirteen days after hatching from the egg. This is true whether the queen results from an egg laid in a preconstructed cell or in a cell built by the bees around a worker larva, or from a larva grafted into a queen cell cup and finished in a cell-building colony. If, for example, a 24-hour-old larva is grafted into a queen cell cup and conditions are favorable for its development, the queen will emerge twelve days later; or, if the bees construct a queen cell around a 48-hour-old larva and rear it into a queen, it will emerge from its cell eleven days later. Provision to take care of the cells must be made before the queens emerge in the cell-building colony.

The appearance of a queen cell frequently indicates its approximate age. Ripe queen cells are well sculptured and the bees usually reduce the thickness of the cap closing the cell. If a ripe queen cell is held before a strong light and tilted slightly to one side, the outline of the image within can be seen quite clearly, and sometimes the movement of legs or wings also can be discerned. Many queen breeders "candle" their cells in this way and thus can be certain of distributing only cells containing living queens to colonies or nuclei.

How to Handle Queen Cells

Queen cells should be handled with great care at all times. Development may be disrupted by heat or cold or by jarring the cells. A sudden jar of unsealed queen cells may dislodge the larvae from their beds of royal jelly, and the wings and legs of pupae in older cells may be injured. A comb containing queen cells should never be shaken if the cells are to be used; the bees should be smoked off or brushed off gently.

The general practice in queen rearing is to remove queen cells from the cell builder and put them into nuclei one or two days before the queens are due to emerge. In this way, the cell serves as an introducing cage, permitting the nucleus to become accustomed to the cell before the queen emerges. If the cells are left in the cell builder longer, a queen may emerge before the cells have been removed. One of her first acts after emergence will then be to tear holes in other queen cells and to sting the inmates to death. Moreover, although she will pay little or no attention to unsealed queen cells or to those recently sealed, the workers will usually discontinue the construction of the unsealed queen cells.

NURSERY CAGES

Sometimes cells are placed in nursery cages until the queens emerge. These cages may be made of wood and wire cloth or of spiraled wire (Fig. 39) or of wire cloth. The wood-and-wire cage is probably the most widely used, but the Rauchfuss cage has greater versatility. The cages need not be provisioned with candy, for the bees of the colony will feed the queens; nurse bees are not needed either with the cells or with the queens.

In other instances, the cells are left on the bars and their frames hung in an incubator until the day before they are due to hatch. While these practices have been in use for many years, a majority of queen breeders prefer to leave the cells with strong cell-finishing colonies until they are ready to be placed in mating nuclei.

After the bees are carefully brushed from the cells, the frame containing the bars of cells is taken into a warm room. The cells are separated from the bars and either placed in cell blocks (ten by two by four inches) with rows of holes for the cells or between layers of cotton or cloth in a box. The cells should be kept warm. They should not be exposed to the sun or to cool winds. Chilling will either kill the queen or delay her emergence, and sometimes results in wing deformities.

If the ripe cells are to be transported in cool weather, some artificial method of keeping them warm should be used. Some beekeepers use bees for this purpose, putting about a pint of them in a honey pail in which the cells are placed on layers of cloth, the pail being ventilated by a few small holes. Others place a warmed and insulated piece of

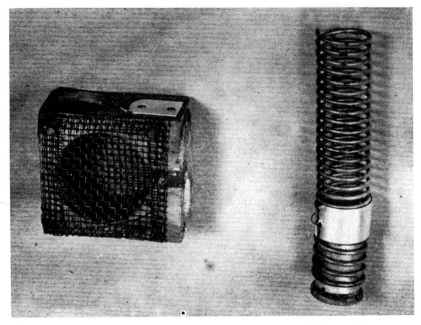

Fig. 39. Alley wood and wire nursery cage, and Rauchfuss spiral nursery cage. (The metal tag has been added to cover the side opening and for record purposes.)

iron or stone beneath the quilts covering the cells. Too much heat, however, is as bad as, or worse than, too little.

Placing the Queen Cells in the Nuclei

Queen cells should be hung in a normal manner between the top bars of two frames in the immediate vicinity of brood, or should be pushed gently into the surface of the comb near brood or where the bees are clustering. If the weather is cool, it is better to place the cells an inch or so below the top bar or where the bees can cluster around the cell and keep it warm.

In all cases, care should be taken to leave the end of the cell free for the queen to cut her way out. The cells should not be crushed at any time, and if they have to be pushed into the comb it is advisable first to crush the comb slightly with the fingers. The bees will fasten the cell in place.

A base of wax with which to handle the cell and to hang it between the frames or to serve as an anchor in the comb is preferable to either wooden cell cups or wooden chips. The bees will cut down the wax base after the queen has emerged, whereas the beekeeper has to remove the wooden cell cups or chips.

CHAPTER IV

Queen-Mating Colonies

IN MAKING DIVISIONS to serve as increase or as mating nuclei, several essential features enabling the colony to take proper care of the cell and of the resultant queen require attention. The first consideration is to have enough bees of different ages to provide an equable temperature for the cell and the queen under prevailing weather conditions. The second and equally important consideration is to have sufficient food present to enable the nurse bees to provide the queen with proper nourishment for her development. A correct balance between number of bees, size of hive or nucleus box, and food for the little colony is very important in the production of good queens.

Making Increase and Use of Full-Sized Hive Bodies for Mating Queens

There are many different ways of making increase to take care of queen cells and at the same time provide a method of producing queens for introduction into full-sized colonies, but only a few need be described.

1. An "increase" can be made by taking enough brood and bees from other colonies to fill a standard eight- or ten-frame hive. If one or two combs of brood and bees are taken from each of four colonies and the balance of the hive is filled with drawn combs, the respective losses will not greatly weaken the other colonies and will provide a new colony that will develop to producing strength within a few weeks. A laying queen or a ripe queen cell can be given to the "divide" within a few hours after it is made up.

2. A colony that is preparing to swarm can be divided so that the queen and most of the unsealed brood is left on the parent stand; the combs of sealed brood are placed in a hive along side of the parent hive, with the entrance turned in the opposite direction. A ripe queen cell

can be given to the new colony made in this way. After the queen has started to lay, the colony can be used as increase, if more colonies are desired, or it can be united with the parent colony after the removal of the older queen, and after all cells, if any, are broken down.

3. In "Demareeing" for swarm control, the top super of brood and bees can be set off on a new stand ten days after the manipulation was first made, then either left with a ripe queen cell or given one prepared by other methods.

4. Two or more frames of brood and bees, with an adequate supply of honey, can be placed in a hive body on top of the parent colony but separated from it by a double-screened division board or by an inner cover with wire cloth screen on each side of the bee-escape hole. The division should be given a small entrance at the back. A ripe queen cell can be placed in the divide within a few hours after it is made. When the resulting queen has started to lay and has established a good brood nest, union with the colony below can be effected simply by removing the screen. If the two queens are separated by a queen excluder, both will continue rearing brood until removal of the queen excluder, after which the younger queen is the more likely to survive. This method is favored by many amateur and commercial beekeepers because it requires a minimum of equipment and provides quick requeening of colonies. It can be used to produce multiple-queen colonies and, if started in late spring, the combined efforts of two good queens will make powerful colonies for summer honey flow.

Use of Nuclei for Mating Queens

Nuclei used as mating hives are of two types: those with standard-sized brood frames in divided eight-frame or ten-frame hive bodies, and shallow frames, divided standard frames, or other special frames. Some of the smaller units are called "baby nuclei."

THE DIVIDED HIVE

A type of nucleus that is quite frequently used for mating queens and which is most adaptable to the needs of the honey producer is the standard hive body divided into two, three, or four separate compartments, each with a separate entrance. The dividing partitions are generally of wood, stripped on the sides and bottom to hold them in

Fig. 40. Standard hive body divided into three 3-frame nuclei by division boards.

place and to make them *bee tight*. Some beekeepers fit these partitions into grooves cut into the end walls of the hive, and then strip the bottom to prevent the board from pulling up when a comb is removed. Closing the compartment tops with individual wood covers or with canvas tacked to the partitions permits opening one compartment at a time.

The entrances should be arranged on the ends and sides, or so that no two are on the same side of the hive. This arrangement helps the queens and bees mark their own entrance and reduces the danger of bees drifting from one nucleus to another.

These nuclei can be made up with a comb of honey and partly filled frames of brood and bees taken from populous colonies. The interchangeable frames facilitate the addition or removal of bees, honey, and brood to keep the nuclei in proper strength. To prevent bees from drifting back to their parent colonies, the nuclei may be made up in one yard and then removed to another. The entrances can be closed with wire cloth or green grass while the nuclei are being formed.

Nuclei can also be made up by assembling combs of brood from one set of colonies and bees from another lot. Each nucleus is then given a comb of honey, one of brood, an empty comb, and about a pound or more of bees, depending on its size. A ripe queen cell is given the nucleus just before the bees are put in. The brood will prevent the bees from absconding and the emerging bees will maintain the strength of the colony until it can rear brood of its own. It is not desirable to have a nucleus of less than two combs.

While it is generally advantageous to use brood in the formation of nuclei, it is not essential, and when large numbers of nuclei are formed it may be impractical. Nuclei formed without brood should either remain closed for three days in a cool dark place before they are put on location, or they should be closed with green grass as they are put out late in the day.

When combs of honey are not available, division-board feeders may be substituted for one of the frames in nuclei having three or more combs. Entrance feeders can also be used, but these frequently encourage robbing.

OTHER TYPES OF NUCLEI FOR MATING QUEENS

Many other types of nuclei are also used for mating queens. Their operation varies according to the nucleus size, but the same fundamental principles govern the use of each type.

1. The nearest approach to the divided hive is the special box divided into two compartments, each large enough to hold three standard Hoffman brood frames. These are quite desirable, for they can be used to rear queens in the honey-producing yards and can be maintained in these yards during the active season. They fit in well with general apiary operations because the combs are standard and readily interchangeable with honey-producing colonies. They are strong enough to winter over in milder climates and are more self-supporting than smaller nuclei.

2. Nuclei made from shallow five and three-eighths inch extracting supers are preferred by some queen breeders. The supers are divided into two to four compartments. They can be divided lengthwise to accommodate the standard shallow extracting frame or crosswise to take a special frame. One type of nucleus made from the eight-frame

Fig. 41. Eight-frame shallow super divided crosswise into two nuclei, with the two-way feeder dividing the nuclei.

shallow extracting super has a double division-board-type feeder separating the super crosswise into two compartments. Each compartment will take five combs with frames five and three-eighths inches deep and eleven and three-fourths long (Fig. 41). These nuclei can be made strong enough to maintain a cluster suitable to taking care of the cells and the queens, and can be stacked on standard eight-frame colonies when not in use. They can be made up by getting regular colonies to fill a sufficient number of the frames with brood and honey to give each nucleus a comb of brood, and a frame of honey. A drawn comb and a frame of foundation are added. A pint of bees is sufficient to form a good cluster over two of the combs. When combs of brood are not available, the nucleus can be made up with queenless bees, in which case they should be kept confined in the nucleus and the nucleus kept in a cool place until the young queen emerges from her cell.

3. A standard ten-frame hive is sometimes divided into four compartments by division boards running lengthwise and crosswise (Fig. 42). The lengthwise division board can incorporate a division-board-

type feeder with four compartments, one for each nucleus. (Use of removable lengthwise boards permits reducing to two compartments, if desired.) Each compartment entrance should be located on a different side of the hive. Frames for this nucleus are made from standard Langstroth end bars and special-length top and bottom bars. Those who use this type of nucleus give as one advantage the fact that one can see the entire surface of the small comb at a glance, thus facilitating finding the queen.

Frames of brood and honey for stocking these nuclei can be obtained by placing some of the bodies on regular hives. Then each nucleus is given a comb of honey, one of brood, one drawn comb, one or two with foundation, and enough bees to cover three combs. The nuclei

Fig. 42. Standard body divided lengthwise and crosswise into four nuclei.

Fig. 43. One type of baby nucleus with queen cell in place between two frames, with a feeder tin at the back.

can be made up without brood and honey, in which case the bees should be confined to the nucleus, which is kept in a cool place for three days before being put on location, and the bees must be fed.

4. Small mating hives containing frames approximately four-by-five inches are usually referred to as *baby nuclei*. They vary considerably in construction and size, but the typical baby nucleus is similar to the one shown in figure 43, a box measuring five and three-quarter inches deep, four and three-quarter inches wide and five and three-quarter inches long on the inside, and with walls three-eighths inch thick. The box holds three four-by-five-inch frames and a feeder. The entrance is a seven-sixteenth-inch hole in the front, near the alighting board. The entrance can be closed with a metal disc and the queen can be confined by a piece of queen excluder. The cover fits down over all sides or simply over the ends. A one-inch screened opening in the back provides ventilation.

The success of baby nuclei depends to a great extent on weather conditions and on how they are managed. Many commercial queen breeders have used them for years. They are inexpensive to make and to operate. For the first round of queens, the nuclei are stocked inside of a building which is kept cool, by an air-conditioning cooler if necessary. A sufficiency of bees is shaken from regular colonies into a ventilated box (Fig. 44), where they are fed copiously on sugar syrup. The bees are sprinkled with thin syrup or water just before transfer to the nuclei. When they are well fed, and thus less inclined to fly, a half pint of bees is dipped out and poured into each of the nuclei, which have been lined up in double tiers and whose feeder tins have been filled with a heavy sugar syrup. A frame has to be removed before the bees are poured in. A ripe queen cell is hung between the frames at the same time and the cover is put in place. The nuclei are then left in the cool, dark room until the third day, when they are moved to their locations. The queens will then have emerged from their cells and each nucleus will be a miniature swarm with a virgin queen. To prevent drifting when the entrances are opened, the nuclei are usually placed in their locations either just at daylight or late in the afternoon. The queen-excluding zinc can be left in front of the entrance until the fifth or sixth day, but then should be opened. Some queen breeders do not use the queen-excluding zinc to confine the queen during this time.

Fig. 44. Ventilated box for holding bees for stocking nuclei with one type of baby nucleus in the background.

During favorable weather conditions, the queens usually begin lay-ing within ten days. Many users of baby nuclei are of the opinion that queens in baby nuclei mate a day or so earlier than those from more populous colonies. The baby nuclei are frequently located in partial shade, two or more in one location with the entrances in different directions. Some are placed on platforms for ease in handling.

About twelve to seventeen days after the cells are inserted, each nucleus is examined and the feeder refilled with heavy sugar syrup. If the queen is laying, either she is caged or the nucleus is marked to indicate the condition of the queen. It is generally expedient to mark only those which are queenless. Usually the queens are left in the nuclei until they have laid in one or two frames, then caged for ship-ment. A ripe queen cell is put in at the same time or on the following morning. If the queen is not laying by the seventeenth day, most queen breeders will pinch her head and insert another queen cell if the strength of the nucleus warrants. Otherwise, the nucleus is taken in and reconditioned.

Some Shortcuts in Establishing Nuclei

When getting bees from populous colonies to make up nuclei in small hives or in baby nuclei, the bees are shaken into a ventilated box capable of holding from fifteen to twenty pounds of bees, which is brought into the workroom where the nuclei are formed (Fig. 44). As was noted earlier, the bees, being well fed and queenless, can be used to fill the nucleus boxes within a few hours.

Some queen breeders make up nuclei by stacking combs in special holders in hive bodies on top of the ventilated cages, arranging the opening of the cage so that the bees cover the frames. If they are left over night, the frames can be separated and put into their boxes the following morning, by which time a desirable number of bees are clinging to the combs. If this method is used, the bees need not be wet down to get the required number into each nucleus.

When standard Langstroth frames are used, brood and honey can be assembled from different colonies and stacked above a queen excluder on a few strong colonies. Within a short time, all of the combs will be covered with bees and can be set over into the nucleus hives. Another way of accomplishing a similar result is to pile the hive bodies of brood on regulation bottom boards and add about five pounds of bees for each hive body of nine combs.

Arrangement of Nuclei

When the nuclei are established, they are taken to mating yards, where they may be placed on the ground or on benches at a height more convenient for working. Nuclei are frequently arranged in pairs, or irregular groupings with the entrances in different directions, with sufficient space between the different groups to prevent drifting of bees or queens. Partial shade is desirable for baby nuclei; if shade is not available naturally, it should be provided artificially. Protection from ant attacks should also be considered, for nuclei which are being fed sugar syrup are particularly vulnerable. Locating nuclei in groups or blocks makes for efficiency in caring for the cells which come off each day or at different intervals. So too does working all of the nuclei in one block on the same day and for the same purpose. Both practices also reduce the number of records which have to be made of the operations.

Maintenance of Nuclei

The time required to take care of nuclei depends considerably on the type of nucleus, the purpose for which it is being maintained, and

Fig. 45. A yard of baby nuclei arranged in blocks for ease in record keeping and working.

floral conditions. At each examination, *all necessary work should be done*. None should be left to some future date.

Many queen breeders prefer nuclei made with standard frames or even the shallow extracting frames which are interchangeable with those in producing colonies and therefore easier to manage. Divided hives containing three, four, or five standard frames are self-supporting in an average location; but, if queens are to be held in them during the main honey flow, they have to be checked at weekly intervals to take away honey or brood. Such nuclei make an ideal place in which to get combs drawn from foundation or from which to make increase during the season. They can be wintered over in the milder climates and divided in the spring to make more nuclei.

The smaller the nucleus, the more care it takes to maintain it in proper condition for queen rearing. The small frames can be assembled in standard equipment at certain times of the year and placed on colonies where they will be filled with honey or brood for future needs. During the summer months, when the weather is hot, it is more difficult to maintain baby nuclei than larger nuclei, for the number of bees is not large enough to cope with the ventilating needs and other requirements of the little colonies. Many queen breeders discontinue them entirely during the hot season. Partial shade is desirable for all small colonies. Use of double covers to provide insulation from the heat helps the colonies keep their hives cool enough to permit normal activities.

It is hard to say just how large or small a nucleus should be. Requirements vary greatly with environmental conditions. A nucleus containing one pound of bees in a hive large enough to permit it to expand without clustering out during warm weather is usually suitable; it can keep the hive cool in partial shade and also keep it warm on the cooler days and nights of early spring. These two fundamentals are highly important in all nuclei. The cost of maintaining a considerable investment in strong nuclei may be overcome to a considerable extent by the amount of useful work such nuclei will do under favorable conditions.

Feeding Nuclei

The best food for nuclei is honey stored in the comb. A nucleus should have ample stores at all times, for it is difficult to rear queens when the mating colonies are short of honey and pollen. During seasons when nectar is scarce or when the nucleus is too small to be self-supporting, the dangers of robbing are greatly enhanced by feeding sugar syrup. When combs of honey are not available, a heavy sugar syrup fed in a feeder enclosed in the nucleus is the best substitute.

In moist climates, a nucleus containing a half pound or more of bees will survive on dry sugar. Under favorable conditions, the nucleus will dissolve it, build comb, and even store the sugar in liquid form in the comb. This method of feeding incites robbing less than any other method when artificial stores have to be supplied. The granulated sugar can be placed in the feeders or poured on the bottom board at the back of the hive. The bees will carry some of the sugar out of the hive, but will use enough of it to maintain the colony.

Methods of supplying sugar syrup to nuclei differ with the size of the operation. Containers for handling the syrup vary from sprinkler cans with the sprinkler head removed, to five-gallon pressure sprayers, and even to spray tanks holding 100 gallons or more, usually equipped with hoses and cutoffs. The last type is used in very large mating yards, where several thousand nuclei have to be fed. Two men apply the feed as a third drives through the apiary.

Mating-Hive Records

Operational records are a necessity whether few nuclei or thousands are operated. Records should be simple and easily kept.

When few nuclei are operated, records may be kept in a notebook with a page devoted to each nucleus or on the top or side of each box. Many types of records have been devised. Some consist of wooden blocks which are shifted to various positions on top of the nucleus to indicate different conditions. Some utilize charts and pointers, or strips of wood or metal of several colors. Perhaps the simplest procedure is to write on the top of the nucleus itself with a heavy crayon. The date the cell is put into the nucleus is recorded, and when the queen is removed for use or shipment a line is drawn through this entry. If it is found that the queen disappeared from the nucleus, the "skip" is indicated by circling the date. If two successive skips occur in a nucleus, it should be remade before another cell is given, as the bees will have become quite old.

When more than a few nuclei are operated, record keeping is greatly simplified and time spent in searching for laying queens is reduced if the nuclei are established in small yards or in blocks in larger yards. A block may consist of enough nuclei to take care of one day's operation. An entire block is established at one time and the block is worked at one time. If the blocks are numbered they are as easily referred to as are single nuclei. Written top records may also be kept on the individual nuclei of a block.

At the time queens are caught from the nuclei, some nuclei will often need feed, brood, bees, or other attention. These needs should be met after the queens are caught and before leaving the yard. The operation is expedited by indicating the various needs at the time they are first discovered. Rocks or clods of dirt placed on the tops serve very well as temporary indicators of the nucleus condition and they can be discarded when the nucleus has been reconditioned.

Robbing

Robbing is one of the most serious problems confronting the queen breeder. It is especially difficult to control when baby nuclei are operated in areas where the spring nectar flow is very light or erratic.

The best robbing control, all beekeepers agree, is prevention. Unless it is absolutely necessary, nuclei should not be worked on days when robbing is almost certain to occur. A minimum of smoke should be used when examining nuclei, and they should not be kept open longer than necessary. Honey, syrup, or bits of comb should not be left on the ground or otherwise exposed to searching bees. Feeding should be done late in the afternoon, and it is preferable to feed by giving combs of honey, which should be placed away from the entrance, or by pouring sugar syrup in a division-board type feeder similarly located.

It is sometimes necessary to catch queens, put out cells, or for other reasons to open the nuclei even when robbers are menacing. The open nucleus may be protected by a damp sack laid across the top while a frame is being examined, and after the nucleus is closed grass can be piled loosely over the entrance. If robbers seriously attack the nucleus they may sometimes be discouraged by laying a wet sack over the top.

The best method of handling robbers, in the experience of the authors, is to work the nuclei within a screened cage four to six feet high and open at the top (Fig. 46). The cage should be wide and long enough to permit the beekeeper to move around freely, and it should be light enough to handle easily. One man can move the cage from one

Fig. 46. Robbing cage, When placed over a nucleus it permits the nucleus to be examined without the anoyance of robbers. (Note the top of the cage is open.)

nucleus to another without getting out of it. Such a cage effectively keeps the robbers away from the nucleus while it is being examined.

Robbers may attack the nucleus when the cage is removed. If the entrance is contracted so only one or two bees can pass through it at a time and if the nucleus body is provided with a separate screened ventilation opening, the nucleus can usually defend itself. If the entrance is the only source of ventilation, the robbers may mass so tightly at the restricted entrance that the bees smother within. When this is a potential danger, a special entrance screen can be used to restrict the entrance while allowing almost full ventilation (Fig. 47). This device is constructed like a small moving screen, and permits the bees to come out of the entrance and crawl over the front of the nucleus. The robbers usually try to gain entrance through the screen and the nucleus

Fig. 47. Robbing screen, which allows the bees a restricted entrance but full ventilation.

bees guard the very small opening which is left as an entrance. The device has proved very successful, and in areas where robbing is often serious it might be advantageous to fit each nucleus with one as well as to work the nuclei within a cage routinely.

CHAPTER V

The Care of Queens

ALTHOUGH THE MAIN SCOPE of this book is the discussion of factors related to the production of queens, the care and replacement of queens is so closely associated with queen rearing and with successful honey production that a brief consideration of these subjects is relevant.

General Practices

Since the queen is the most important individual in a colony, frames and supers, as we have repeatedly emphasized, must be handled in a manner calculated to prevent her injury. In handling frames, it is essential to avoid crushing the queen between the shoulders of the frames, between burr combs on uneven surfaces of the combs, or against the sides of the hives. If a comb containing the queen is placed on the outside during examination of the hive, the frame should be leaned against the hive and turned so that the queen is on the shaded underside. It is even safer to place two combs of brood on the outside with the queen between them. In replacing the combs, a quick glance at the space where the combs rested will determine whether the queen has crawled or accidentally fallen from the combs, as sometimes happens.

Queens in cages should never be exposed to the direct rays of a hot sun. This, as was noted earlier, applies to queen cells too. Queens and cells are also easily chilled, and, if colonies have to be examined during cold weather, both queens and queen cells should be kept in the warm parts of the hives and not exposed to cold.

Colonies should not be examined when they have virgin or newly introduced queens or queens which have just mated, if such examinations can be avoided. Such queens and their attending bees are nervous, and the disturbance of jarring or of opening a hive may cause the workers to "ball" the queen. When this occurs, one or more bees will attack the queen and attempt to sting her. Other bees will join in the affair, biting and pulling at her legs and wings. Soon a ball of bees will be formed tightly around the queen, all apparently intent on doing her bodily harm. Queens frequently come out of the experience with a broken leg or some other injury, or may be killed, although occasionally they escape bodily harm.

Should balling occur while working a hive, one way to break it up is to pick up the ball of bees on the end of the hive tool and drop it in water. The bees will immediately disperse and the wet queen can be put back on the combs and the hive closed. If a can of talcum powder is handy, the perfumed powder can be sprinkled liberally over the ball of bees and adjacent comb. This generally disperses the ball and prevents recurrence. Or the ball of bees and the entire colony can be given a good smoking before the hive is closed.

How to Find Queens

Much time can be lost in an unnecessary search for queens in honey producing colonies. Queens should be judged more by their work than by appearances, and one can tell more about a queen by examining her brood and its distribution in the hive than by looking at her on the combs. At certain times, however, it is necessary to find the queen. A few suggestions in the matter might be helpful.

Various manipulations in producing honey are facilitated by confining the queen to one or two brood chambers by use of a queen excluder. If the brood chamber consists of but one hive body, any supers above the queen excluder can be set off and the excluder removed. Before placing the excluder on top of the supers, it should be examined quickly to see if, by chance, the queen is on it. Then, using no more smoke than is necessary to control the bees, a comb is removed from the side or center of the brood nest, whichever is the easier. If it contains unsealed brood, a rapid glance over the bees is in order to see if the queen is on it. If she is not, the frame is stood on end against the opposite side of the hive, and each comb is examined in turn after glancing down over the sides of the combs next to it. Starting from the center of the brood chamber and proceeding alternately to combs on each side of the center is likely to facilitate finding the queen more quickly than if the combs are taken in order from either side.

The queen usually is surrounded by a number of bees headed toward her, and as she moves across the combs the bees give way from in front of her. This arrangement of bees frequently strikes the eye about as quickly as one sees the queen, and it aids in locating her on the comb.

If the brood nest consists of two brood chambers, the top chamber is removed to allow a view of the bottom one. If eggs and larvae are present, then the lower chamber is examined, as above. If the queen is not found there the second story should be examined before it is replaced on the first. If it is set back in position before being examined, the queen might run down into the bottom chamber during the examination.

When the queen has the free run of three or more stories, one should start at the top to see if brood is present. This can be done by tipping up the super and peering at the combs from beneath or by removing one or two center combs. This procedure should be followed with the other hive bodies until the active center of the brood nest is located, where the queen will usually be found.

If the queen cannot be found by these direct methods, although eggs indicate that she is present, the bees can be shaken from the combs into an empty hive body and driven with an occasional puff of smoke through a queen excluder into a super of combs below. Each comb should be examined after most of the bees have been shaken off, and then should be set on the outside of the hive until all of the combs have been shaken. A glance now and then at the bees on the queen excluder may locate the queen.

Some commercial beekeepers force the bees out of the upper stories and into the lower brood chamber by the use of a repellent or smoke and then insert the queen excluder between the lower brood chamber and supers. Four days later, the presence of eggs will indicate the location of the queen, with the search generally limited to the lower chamber.

Locating Virgin Queens

The absence of eggs and the presence of the telltale mark of a queen cell from which a queen has recently emerged or queen cells which have been torn down frequently indicate that a virgin queen is present. Young virgin queens are not regarded as highly by the bees as are laying queens and do not have a retinue of nurse bees around them. They are also smaller and are more prone to run and hide than are laying queens. They may even try to fly if an attempt to catch them fails. If careful examination of the combs fails to locate her, forcing the bees to go through a queen excluder is probably the quickest way to find a virgin queen in a populous colony.

Since nuclei are but small colonies used in rearing queens, they have fewer frames and bees than the larger hives, and their queens are much easier to find. A glance down between the combs of a nucleus will indicate where the brood is likely to be, and the comb with the greatest number of bees can be examined first. Very little, if any, smoke need be used in examining nuclei, and the queen is likely to be on the combs. If she cannot be found there, then all frames must be removed and the search extended to the sides and bottom of the box. Before caging the queen for use or shipment, it should be determined that she is laying normally.

Catching Queens

It is usual to catch a queen in order to cage her or to clip and mark her. If she is to be caged, she should be caught from behind by slipping the thumb and index finger down over the side of her thorax and abdomen and grasping her by the wings, without pressing on the abdomen. She can then be placed in a queen cage by inserting her head

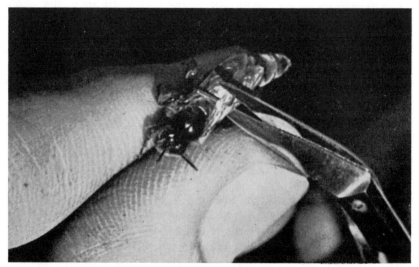

Fig. 48. Proper way to hold a queen for clipping or marking.

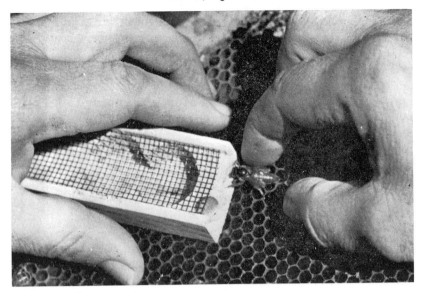

Fig. 49. Herding queen into queen cage.

and forelegs in the end opening, giving her a gentle push with the middle finger before entirely releasing her wings.

If the queen is to be clipped and marked, she should be placed on the left forefinger while she is still being held by the wings. Thus two pairs of legs on one side can be grasped between the thumb and forefinger of the left hand (Fig. 48). Grasping two of her legs prevents the queen from twisting and breaking a leg while she is being clipped by a fine pair of scissors. It is best to clip off about one half of the right or left wings, leaving the other pair to pick her up with in the future.

A queen may be caged safely by "herding" her into the end hole of the cage placed in front of her while she is crawling on the comb. The forefinger and thumb of one hand direct her movement from the rear, while the other hand holds the cage in place (Fig. 49).

Marking Queens

Queens are marked to facilitate locating them or for conveying information about their age or breeding. A bright spot of color, such as vermilion, light green, or yellow, on the top of her thorax makes a queen stand out on a comb rather conspicuously. This is especially true of the dark races of bees. Fingernail polish, a quick-drying lacquer like automobile touch-up lacquer, or a dry pigment mixed with alcohol and shellac or with celluloid dissolved in acetone, make satisfactory media.

The Eckhardt queen-marking tool is a good device for marking queens, although its use is time consuming. The tool consists of a small metal tube, which cuts out a small circular disc of paper, and a plunger which pushes the disc against a small spot of glue placed on the thorax of the queen. Use of bright, colored luminous paper on which numbers have been printed helps systematize identification of queens.

Colors applied to different portions of the queen's thorax or second segment of her abdomen can indicate such factors as age, breeding, origin, etc.; two or more colors can be used for detailed information. Care should be taken to prevent any pigment from getting on the neck of the queen or covering any of the spiracles on her thorax or abdomen. If properly applied, a good lacquer will not injure the queen and will serve as a distinguishing mark for as long as she lives. Pigments containing banana oil sometimes excite bees when the queen is returned to the comb, but holding the queen a few seconds until the lacquer dries and some of the odor is dissipated minimizes this problem.

Considerable time is saved in finding queens of the black races if they are allowed to emerge in nursery cages and are then marked before being introduced as virgin queens into mating nuclei.

A beginner could benefit by practicing marking and clipping technique on drones.

The Introduction of Queens

The first rule in introducing a queen into a colony is to be sure that the colony is queenless. Any queen cells which may have been started during a period of queenlessness must be destroyed. The second rule is that after the new queen has been introduced the colony must not be disturbed until she has had time to establish a brood nest. A safe margin is about ten days. A queenless colony is more excitable than a queenright colony and does not lose all of its nervousness until after it has brood in all stages. A newly introduced young queen is also somewhat excitable until she has had time to lay normally, without disturbance, for several days. The third consideration of importance in introducing a queen is that she be placed in the brood nest of the colony in a manner that will give her the colony odor or provide some protection for her until the bees become accustomed to her odor and presence. Queens are introduced quite readily during a nectar flow, less successfully when bees are prone to rob. Success is most likely if the queen is introduced into a broodless hive or one containing only sealed brood.

As a general rule, queens can be introduced successfully if the colony is made queenless and the queen introduced by the cage method at the same operation. This practice lends itself to economic operation of colonies and is used by many beekeepers.

CAGE METHODS OF INTRODUCTION

The queen usually is shipped in a Benton mailing cage, which consists of a wooden, screen-covered cage with three communicating compartments, one of which is filled with queen-cage candy. This cage may also serve as an introducing cage. In shipment, the queen is accompanied by ten or twelve worker bee attendants. Since the colony may show animosity toward the strange worker bees, it is desirable to remove them before placing the queen and her cage in the colony, although it is not absolutely necessary to do so. The removal of these bees should be done inside a room or enclosure, for the queen is usually light enough in weight to fly, and may escape if the workers are released in the open.

The queen cage usually has a piece of thin cardboard over the candy hole. (Queens received in package bees may have the candy hole closed with a cork or a piece of metal.) It generally is desirable to remove any restriction over the candy opening before the cage is placed in the hive.

After the colony has been made queenless and the worker bees have been removed from the cage, it can be placed on its side between the top bars of two frames in the brood chamber. If the colony has a two-story brood chamber, the cage can be placed between the bottom bars of the second brood chamber, or the cage can be stood on end, candy end up, on the bottom board of the hive, between two combs of brood. Whatever the position, the bees in the colony should have access to the wire screen of the cage in order to become acquainted with the queen and to permit them to feed her through the wire. It will usually take the bees from 24 to 48 hours to eat a hole through the candy large enough for the queen to get through.

Several different types of introducing cages can be used (Fig. 50).

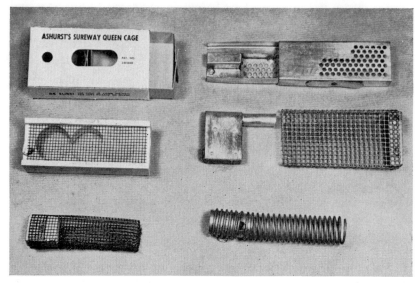

Fig. 50. Various types of introducing cages.

Some have special merits to increase the probability of success in introducing queens. For example, one type of introducing cage has two food compartments, one shorter than the other and covered with a queen-excluding zinc; the other is large enough, when the food is eaten out, to permit the escape of the queen.

Another type of cage embodies the idea of caging the queen beneath a paper box which is pushed a quarter of an inch into the surface of an area of a comb containing emerging brood and a few cells of honey. The bees will feed the queen through small holes in the ends of the cage and will cut under it, as well as through it, and thus release the queen. This is an improvement on the old method of imprisoning the queen under a wire screen box pushed into the comb in a similar manner, for the bees can cut and remove the paper box without injuring the comb.

Direct Methods of Introduction

Several methods of requeening a hive without using cages are used successfully by many beekeepers.

The Spray Method. In the spray method, colonies are made queenless and, in the same operation, the sides and tops of the frames in the brood chamber are sprayed with a fine mist of sugar syrup, which is also used to wet the queen in her cage thoroughly. The queen is then released directly on top of the combs and given another spraying of syrup as she crawls down between the combs. The hive is then closed. One bad feature of this method is that in cleaning the queen of the sugar syrup the bees sometimes remove some of her hair, thus making her look older than she actually is. The method should not be used when it will instigate robbing.

The Smoke Method. When the smoke method is used, after the colony has been made queenless the new queen is run in at the entrance of the hive, followed by several generous puffs of smoke. This method works best when the new queen is taken from a nucleus only a few minutes before she is introduced into her new hive.

The Powder Method. One of the principles involved in the safe introduction of a queen is that she must acquire the hive odor before she is accepted as one of the colony. A method has been developed which temporarily gives both the colony and the queen an identical odor. This is accomplished by dusting a strongly perfumed talcum powder over the frames of the brood chamber and over the newly introduced queen. Unless she has been clipped, there is danger of the queen flying when released from the cage in which she has been confined for three or more days.

Transfer of Combs of Brood and Bees. When queens are reared in standard nuclei in an apiary which also has producing colonies, still another method is useful. A colony is made queenless, and three frames of brood and bees from a nucleus, with their laying queen on the inside combs, is set over into the queenless hive in exchange for a similar number of combs. This method is generally successful if the combs are placed next to the wall of the brood chamber. If the colony has brood in two or three hive bodies, the combs from the nucleus should be set in the top brood chamber next to the side. The bees of the colony gradually mix with those set in, usually without any fighting, and the queen continues to lay in her own combs, gradually extending her activities to all sections of the brood area in the hive. Separation of the transferred combs on the inner side, bottom, and top by a single thickness of newspaper adds to the success of this method.

Uniting Full Colonies. Swarm control and requeening may be combined in one operation. Shortly before normal colonies make preparations to swarm, each is divided and the queenless portion given a ripe queen cell produced in anticipation of the need. All colonies can be left to build up as fast as conditions permit until the beginning of the main honey flow, when they are united to make the original number. The brood chamber containing the young queen and her bees is set on top of the brood chamber of a colony containing an old queen, the two being separated simply by the thickness of a sheet of newspaper. Many beekeepers unite such colonies merely by smoking both thoroughly and setting the one with the younger queen on top of the other. The newspaper method is the safest procedure under a wider range of environmental conditions, however. A few holes punched in the newspaper will hasten its removal by the bees. If the colonies are united in late afternoon by the newspaper method, very few bees will return to their former location. Drifting of bees will be negligible if in making the divisions the new colonies are located next to the parent colony. Both queens may continue to lay for a number of days or weeks, thus adding to the general strength of the colony during the honey flow.

A modification of this method is used by many commercial beekeepers as a means of requeening and strengthening their colonies for the honey flow. A two-story colony is divided, with most of the sealed brood and adhering bees being placed to one side, leaving the queen and combs of unsealed brood in the lower brood chamber. A queen excluder is placed over the brood chamber of the parent colony, then a super of combs is added, and on top of the super a double-screened cover with one-half to three-quarters of an inch between the two screens. The hive body containing the sealed brood and bees is next set on top of the screened division board and the top cover put in place. The top colony is given a small entrance to the rear and provided with a ripe queen cell or a young laying queen. When the top colony has a well-established brood nest, the screened division board can be removed and the top colony set on top of the lower brood chamber, with the queen excluder placed between it and the supers. The old queen can be killed or simply left to be replaced by the younger queen, in which case both queens may continue to lay for a considerable period.

The Storage of Queens

In the production of queens and package bees, there are times when queens are being produced faster than they can be shipped and it is necessary to remove them from the nuclei and hold them a few days. Honey producers also occasionally need to hold surplus queens for short periods before introducing them into their colonies.

The conditions for storing queens will vary with the length of time they have to be held. Queens can be maintained in mailing cages, with attendants, for two or more weeks without apparent injury if they are kept at approximately brood-rearing temperatures (85°F to 93°F), and have access to queen-cage candy *and water*.[1] Queens and attendants will not live as long without access to water. They should be kept out of the sun and away from dust and ants. The relative humidity is not too important, but 20 to 50 per cent is better than a higher humidity. The lower the relative humidity, the greater will be the demand for water, but there is no apparent advantage to humidity over 50 per cent. It appears that bees need water more to maintain the balance of water in their bodies than merely to soften the candy.

While queen breeders can set up a thermostatically controlled incubator and regulate the humidity as well, the electric controls and source of heat are subject to failure. Furthermore, a strong colony can control its temperature and humidity, as well as the food supply, to better advantage of the caged queens than can be done artificially. Consequently, beekeepers store surplus queens in *queenless portions* of strong colonies. This can be done without apparent injury to the queens, and possibly with benefit, for a period of several weeks' duration.

It is undesirable to have attendants in the cages of queens held in storage in colonies, for the bees will tend to be more antagonistic when attendants are included. The workers will feed the queens through the wire screen of the cages and thus provide them with a more natural food than when they have access to queen-cage candy alone.

A queen reservoir can be made in the second or third story of a hive in which the queen is confined to the lower chamber by an excluder.

---

[1] Woodrow, A. W. 1941. Some effects of temperature, relative humidity, confinement, and type of food on queens in mailing cages. U.S.D.A. Mimeo. Series E-529.

Frames of larvae on both sides of each frame holding queens in cages aid in the maintanance of uniform temperature and tend to provide an adequate number of nurse bees to feed the queens. Queens survive as well if held in two-hole foodless and attendantless cages in colony reservoirs as when they have a large cage with queen-cage candy. It seems desirable to feed the holding colony while the queens are in storage, although queens have been wintered over, experimentally, in strong queenless colonies whose natural comb stores were not supplemented.

Special frames may be made to hold a double row of queen cages placed back to back in each of two or three tiers (Fig. 51). In this way, 48 three-hole cages or 78 two-hole cages can be placed in a standard frame with a wider bottom bar and pieces of equal width between the tiers. Three or four frames can be placed in each queen reservoir colony, although using fewer risks less expense should anything go wrong.

As an added precaution, the reservoir compartment should have no opening to the outside through which a virgin queen or stray swarm might enter.

If queens are to be held in storage during periods when the colony

Fig. 51. Caged queen in a special frame for storing in a queen reservoir colony.

will not be strong enough to maintain a satisfactory cluster over all the queen cages, it is desirable to use empty cages in the outside row of the holding frame. While queen breeders do not, as a general practice, attempt to carry surplus queens in reservoirs over the winter period, it is conceivable that this method of storage could be perfected to a point where it would be more economical and better than using nuclei which might not be strong enough to maintain a satisfactory temperature during the colder portions of the year.

When only a few queens need to be carried over for short periods of time, it can be done satisfactorily by placing them in an empty shallow super on top of a cell-building colony or a strong colony in which the queen is confined to the lower story by an excluder. Every hole in each queen cage should be closed by a metal disc, or the cage must be stored so that the worker bees cannot release the queen by eating through the candy compartment or other material used to close either opening.

Effect of Confinement on a Laying Queen

One argument in favor of holding queens in a queen reservoir for a short period before shipping them by mail is that the queens are subjected to a less drastic change in food than when they are caged from their broodnest and shipped immediately. More research is needed to show the effect of confinement as well as of artificial foods on laying queens. Any sudden change from natural food and a state of active laying in a uniform temperature to a small cage, artificial food, and temperatures which may range from 20 to 30 degrees lower, certainly cannot do the queen any good. We know that she continues to lay eggs for 24 to 48 hours after being confined to her cage and will start to lay again within a few hours to several days after she is introduced into a colony. If the change is made during the broodless period, as in late fall, the queen will not lay until brood rearing begins normally in the spring. What becomes of the eggs which are in the process of being formed when a queen is caged or deprived of her regular food (royal jelly) is still a matter of conjecture.

See Nosema Disease, pp. 156–157.

Queen Substance

Soon after a queen is removed from her colony, the bees exhibit considerable restlessness. Unless a queen is restored, queen cells will be started around young larvae. Butler[2] determined that the healthy queen is able to produce a material, which he called "queen substance," that enables the bees to know of her presence in the colony, while a failing queen apparently is unable to produce a sufficient amount of the substance to prevent the bees from starting supersedure queen cells. He speculated that the substance is secured from the queen's body by a minimum number of bees, who add it to their food and distribute it by mouth-to-mouth method, to other bees in the colony.

Subsequently, the source of the queen substance was discovered by Butler and Simpson[3] to be largely in the mandibular gland of the queen. It was thought that the queen distributed the substance over her body when she cleaned herself, the bees securing it when they stroked the queen with their tongues. But this method of dissemination does not explain why the absence of the queen is detected so quickly after her removal. Most beekeepers know that bees are attracted by the odor of crushed queens, or even by the odor of queens in queen cages before any contact has occurred.

Gary[4] found that queens became less attractive when the mandibular glands were removed. He also reported [5] that worker bees became antagonistic to other workers in the same colony when a small portion of the contents of the mandibular gland of a queen was placed on their bodies. Bees which came in direct contact with these "tainted" bees were also attacked by still others, just as queens are attacked in a strange colony. The chemical composition of the substance has been determined as 9-oxodec-2-enoic acid: it has been synthesized by Callow and Johnston.[6] Although excellent advantages in some phases of the beekeeping industry can be imagined, practical uses for products including this substance remain to be determined.

---

[2] Butler, C. B. 1954. The method and importance of the recognition by a colony of honeybees (*A. mellifera*) of the presence of its queen. Trans. R. Ent. Soc. London. 105, pt. 2.

[3] Butler, C. G. and J. Simpson. 1958. The source of the queen substance of the honeybee (*Apis mellifera*). Proc. R. Ent. Soc. Lond. 33:120–2.

[4] Gary, N. E. 1960. Mandibular gland extirpation in living queen and worker honeybees. Bee World 41:229.

[5] Gary, N. E. 1961. Queen honeybee attractiveness as related to mandibular gland secretion. Science, 133(3463):1479–80.

[6] Callow, R. W. and N. C. Johnston. 1960. The chemical constitution and synthesis of queen substance of honeybees (*Apis mellifera*). Bee World 41:152.

CHAPTER VI

Breeding and Stock Improvement

Superior queens cannot be produced by good queen-rearing methods alone. The quality of the stock is fully as important as the manipulative practices. This chapter and the following one are concerned with stock improvement. To the beekeeper who has had no formal biological training these chapters may be somewhat difficult to understand, for they involve terms and material with which the beekeeper is ordinarily not familiar. They are not, however, beyond the grasp of anyone who will study them carefully, and we believe that the beekeeper who is sincerely interested in improving his stock would do well to make a serious study of at least this chapter on breeding and stock improvement.

Technical terms used in these discussions will give the reader little difficulty if he bears in mind that technical words are nothing more than names, and that they are often the only names which are suitable. If technical words were not used, it would be necessary to repeat tedious descriptions which would complicate the narrative and make for monotonous reading. If the meaning of a technical word is learned when the word is first encountered, the term quickly becomes a part of the reader's vocabulary, and as his vocabulary grows he finds he can read and understand technical descriptions and discussions more readily than before.

Breeding, Selection, and Inheritance

Breeding, as used here, is the systematic mating of selected individuals to produce offspring which possess characteristics considered desirable. The matings are made, therefore, with a definite goal in view, and purposeful matings are continued through successive generations. Breeding differs from *rearing* very clearly: rearing is the production of individuals from the egg to the adult, and is not necessarily concerned with parentage of the individuals produced, nor with their characteristics or the characteristics of their offspring.

Selection involves evaluation of the individual based on the determination of their characteristics and of their ability to transmit *factors* which produce these and other characteristics in their offspring. Selection is an important part of any breeding program. The transmission of factors from parent to offspring is called *inheritance*.

The sequential procedures of selecting, breeding, and again selecting is much the same as those for other organisms. All are subject to the same basic laws and mechanisms of heredity which govern passage of various features from parent to offspring. Before breeding methods can be understood and intelligently applied, it is desirable to examine these mechanisms.

The Physical Basis of Inheritance

All organisms are made up of *cells*, small units of living material, and their products. The bee's body is composed, in part, of a very great number of cells; cell-manufactured substances constitute most of the rest of the body. The body wall of a bee, for instance, was manufactured by the layer of cells which lie against the inner surface.

Although different cells of a bee have taken on various forms and functions, each is composed of a basic viscous complex mixture of substance called *protoplasm,* which is encased in a wall, or membrane. The protoplasm is divided into *cytoplasm* and a more-or-less spherical *nucleus* within the cytoplasm (Fig. 52). The nucleus is likewise encased in a membrane. The cytoplasm has various bodies and inclusions, which we need not consider in detail here. Our main concern is with the nucleus.

The nucleus contains a material which stains more deeply with certain dyes than do other cell parts. This material is arranged in a network throughout the nucleus. It is called *chromatin,* and it bears the *genes* (factors), too small to be seen with a microscope, which in cooperation with the environment determine which characters will appear in the offspring.

The growth of an organism involves an increase in the number of cells of the body. Each cell must be complete and must have the same

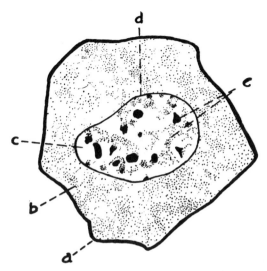

Fig. 52. A. cell. *a,* cell wall; *b,* cytoplasm; *c,* nucleus; *d,* nuclear membrane; *e,* chromatin network.

genes as every other cell. Thus, organism growth requires some mechanism which produces an increased number of cells, each provided with an identical chromatin network. This is accomplished by each cell dividing into two, a process called *mitosis.* In turn, each daugther cell divides, and this process continues until the pattern of development is complete.

When a cell divides by mitosis (Fig. 53), the strands of the chromatin network thicken, forming a long thread which finally separates into individual segments known as *chromosomes.*[1] Sometimes the thread splits longitudinally before the chromosomes become recognizable; if not, the chromsomes split longitudinally after separation. In either event each chromosome has duplicated itself so the cell now has twice the number of chromosomes as before (Fig. 52 B). The membrane of the nucleus disappears and structures, which look like contractile fibers, form a spindle-shaped pattern across the nucleus, with the ends lying in the cytoplasm of the cell. The chromosomes arrange themselves across the middle of this spindle and the halves of each doubled

---

[1] The number, size, and shape of the chromosomes are constant for any particular kind of organism, and if they possess distinctive shapes or sizes they can be visually identified. Each chromosome carries particular genes, which are too small to be seen.

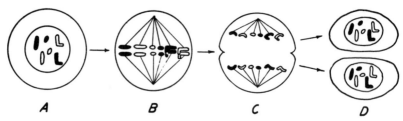

Fig. 53. Mitotic cell division (diagrammatic). *a.* Cell with the full number of chromosomes (represented in this diagram by six, or three pairs). The solid chromosomes may be considered to have come from the queen's mother, and the lighter chromosomes to have come from the queen's father. Thus each chromosome pair is made up of a chromosome from the queen's mother and a chromosome from the queen's father. *b.* The nuclear membrane has disappeared, a spindle has formed, the chromosomes have arranged themselves across the spindle, and each has split lengthwise. *c.* The halves of each chromosome have separated and have gone to opposite ends of the spindle. *d.* A nuclear membrane has formed around each group of chromosomes, and the cell has divided into two cells. Each daughter cell has exactly the same kind of chromosomes.

chromosome separate and go to opposite ends of the spindle. A membrane appears around each group of chromosomes, forming a nucleus, and a new cell wall, which develops across the middle of the spindle, separates the two new nuclei into new cells. In each, the spindle disappears and the chromosomes go through the reverse process to form a thread and a chromatin network.

This process has the utmost significance. By it a single cell divides into two cells which have exactly the same hereditary factors, for each daughter cell gets half of each chromosome which carries the factors.

The cells continue to divide as the organism develops, and the resulting cells come to perform different duties. In the bee some form the brain, others the intestine, and still others form the layer of cells which produce the exoskeleton, or body covering. Certain cells, however, may have been set aside early in the development of the bee; they take no part in the development of the bee itself but are reserved for the propagation of the next generation. These reproductive cells are called *germ cells.* They eventually come to lie in the *ovaries* or *testes* of the bee.

THE GERM CELLS

The germ cells of the queen honey bee develop into the *eggs,* and the germ cells of the drone develop into the *spermatozoa,* known collectively as *gametes*. The queen may lay many thousand eggs during her lifetime; the drone produces about ten million spermatozoa. The mature gametes are derived from germ cells located in the closed ends of the ovarioles of the queen's ovaries and the closed ends of the testes tubules of the drone. The germ cells increase in number by mitotic cell division, but before they become gametes and are functional they must undergo a process called *maturation*.

The body cells and the unmatured germ cells of a queen (or worker) honey bee have 32 chromosomes which, in the non-dividing cell, are arranged into the chromatic network of the nucleus. These chromosomes are *paired;* that is, each chromosome has a mate of identical size and shape. One member of the pair came from the mother of the female bee, through the egg, and the other member came from the

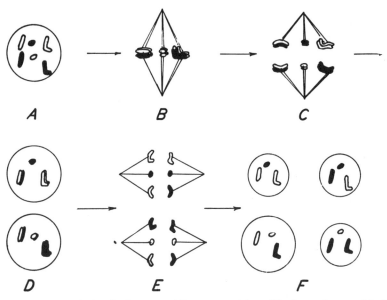

Fig. 54. Meiosis in the bee egg (diagrammatic). *a.* Nucleus of egg with full numbers of chromosomes. Chromosomes represented by six, or three pairs. *b.* Chromosomes of each pair have come together on its spindle and each has split thus forming tetrads. *c.* The four chromosomes of each tetrad separate by pairs, two chromosomes of each tetrad going to one end of the spindle and two going to the opposite end. *d.* Two groups of chromosomes result. *e.* A new spindle forms across each group of chromosomes and the two members of each chromosome pair separate and go to opposite ends of the spindle. *f.* Four nuclei are formed. One is the pronucleus of the egg and survives. The other three are polar bodies and disintegrate.

father, through the spermatozoon which fertilized the egg. The two mates of a chromosome pair are called *homologous* chromosomes; each chromosome is the *homologue* of the other.

There are then 16 pairs of homologous chromosomes in the cells of the female bee. These form two *sets* of 16 chromosomes each, a set consisting of one chromosome from each pair. Such an organism is said to be *diploid*. (The drone, which has one set, is said to be *haploid*.) When the egg matures, which occurs about the time it is laid, one member of each pair of chromosomes is eliminated from the nucleus, leaving the egg with one chromosome set. This is accomplished by a process of division of the nucleus of the egg called *meiosis*.

Meiosis in the bee egg consists of two successive nuclear divisions (Fig. 54), which occur in a sequence similar to that of mitosis. Chromosomes develop from the chromatin network, the nuclear membrane disappears, and division spindles form. However, meiosis takes place in the egg about the time it is laid, and the egg itself does not divide into two eggs. There are, therefore, nuclear divisions without complete cell divisions. Moreover, the chromosomes of maternal origin and the chromosomes of paternal origin at this time come close together on the spindle of the first division, forming 16 *pairs* of homologous chromosomes. This intimate pairing of homologous chromosomes is known as *synapsis*. During synapsis, or prior to it, the homologous chromosomes of each pair split, yielding four chromosomes, instead of two, closely associated as a group. Each such group is a *tetrad*. At this time there may be an exchange of segments between homologous chromosomes, chromosomes from the mother exchanging segments with the chromosomes from the father. This exchange is known as *crossing over,* the mechanism whereby groups of genes on a particular chromosome can be exchanged for groups of similar genes on its homologue.

Two of the chromosomes of *each* tetrad now go to each end of the division spindle. A new spindle appears across each chromosome group, and the two chromosomes of each tetrad which had gone together to one end of the first division spindle now separate and go to opposite ends of the new spindle. This results in four nuclei in the egg, all of which have half the original number of chromosomes, but with a chromosome from each original pair. Only one of the four nuclei survives; it is called the egg *pronucleus*. The other three, known as *polar bodies,* disintegrate. The egg pronucleus unites with a sperm nucleus if the egg is fertilized, or develops independently if the egg is not fertilized. In either case it gives rise to the bee larva by repeated mitotic divisions.

As mentioned above, the 32 chromosomes of a female bee are paired. One member of each pair comes from the mother of the queen through the egg, the other member from the father through the spermatozoon which united with the egg. At meiosis it is a matter of chance which mate of a particular chromosome pair goes to one or the other end of the division spindle with a particular mate of another pair, but the two mates of any one pair never go to the same end of the spindle. They always separate and go to opposite ends.

The body cells and the germ cells of the drone have 16 chromosomes, for the drone develops from an unfertilized egg which has only one set of 16 chromosomes. Before male germ cells can fertilize an egg, they must undergo development from the early male germ cells, which resemble morphologically unspecialized cells, to spermatozoa, each of which has a narrow *head* containing the chromosomes in a greatly condensed state and a long thin *tail* which by a waving motion propels the spermatozoon. During the course of this development, incomplete meiotic divisions occur (Fig. 55). A spindle forms and the chromosomes arrange themselves across the spindle and move apart, but the nuclear membrane does not disappear and the nucleus does not divide. Thus the nucleus keeps its full set of 16 chromosomes. Immediately following this abortive reduction division, another spindle forms at an angle to the preceding one. The chromosomes split and arrange themselves across the spindle, the nuclear membrane disappears, the chromosome halves separate and move toward opposite spindle ends, and the cell divides into two cells with 16 chromosomes in each. However, one of the cells retains most of the protoplasm of the parent cell; this cell develops into the spermatozoon. The smaller cell begins to develop into a spermatozoon, but it never matures.

FERTILIZATION OF THE EGG

The uniting of a male and female gamete is called *fertilization*. The resulting cell is a *zygote*. The upper end of the bee egg has a minute opening which was left when the egg cytoplasm, which had abutted against the nurse cells of the egg follicle, withdrew into the egg. This opening, the *micropyle,* serves as an entry way for the spermatozoa, which are stored in the *spermatheca* of the mated queen. A few spermatozoa at a time are withdrawn from the spermatheca and sent down

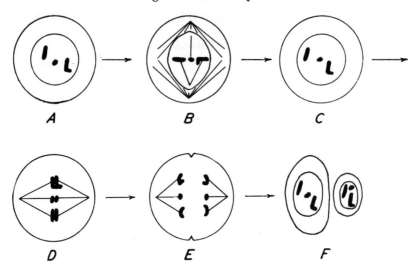

Fig. 55. Maturation division during formation of spermatozoa in the bee (diagrammatic). *a.* Early reproductive cell of drone. Drone cells have half as many chromosomes as cells of the queen or worker, and in this diagram the chromosomes are represented by three chromosomes. *b.* Division spindle forms but nuclear membrane does not disappear, and *c.* cell does not divide. *d.* A second spindle forms, the chromosomes split and arrange themselves across the spindle, and the nuclear membrane disappears. *e.* The halves of each chromosome separate and go to opposite ends of the spindle. *f.* Two cells are formed each with the same number of chromosomes as the original cell and one develops into a spermatozoon. The other cell disappears.

the spermathecal duct by the action of the sperm pump. When the egg is laid by the queen, it passes the end of the spermathecal duct on the way through the vagina. If it is destined to become a female bee, it apparently is held in the vagina for an instant while the micropyle is pressed against the opening of the spermathecal duct until one or more spermatozoa enter the egg. The egg is then deposited in the cell.

After the spermatozoa enter the egg they undergo a transformation (Fig. 56). The tails disappear, the heads enlarge, and they again take on the appearance of nuclei. They spread out in the upper end of the egg and move downward in the cytoplasm while the egg is undergoing maturation. As soon as the egg maturation divisions are finished, the pronucleus begins to move across the egg cytoplasm and it meets one of the sperm nuclei in its path. The two nuclei come close together,

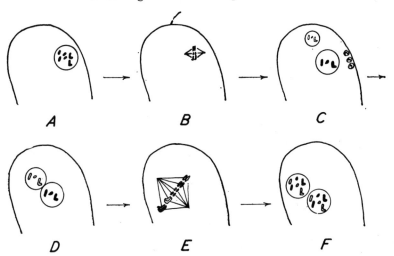

Fig. 56. Fertilization of the bee egg (diagrammatic). *a.* Egg, prior to being laid, with full number of chromosomes (only 6 chromosomes, or 3 pairs, are shown). *b.* Maturation divisions in progress as egg is laid. Spermatozoa enter egg. *c.* Maturation divisions finished. Pronucleus now has only half the original number of chromosomes. Sperm head has again taken on appearance of nucleus. *d.* Sperm nucleus and egg pronucleus meet. *e.* Chromosomes of the two nuclei split and arrange themselves across spindle. Halves of each chromosome separate and go to opposite ends of the spindle. *f.* A nuclear membrane has formed around each group of chromosomes and there are now two nuclei each with the full number of chromosomes.

a division spindle forms across them, the nuclear membranes disappear, and the chromatin networks give rise to chromosomes which split and align themselves on the spindle. The chromosome halves then separate and go to opposite ends of the spindle to form two nuclei, and the development of the bee has begun. The male and female gametes each had 16 chromosomes; their union restored the chromosome number in the zygote to 32.

If the egg is destined to become a male bee, it does not receive spermatozoa as it passes through the vagina. The pronucleus of the matured egg reaches the opposite side of the egg without encountering a sperm nucleus. It then divides by mitosis to begin the development of the drone. The matured egg nucleus had only 16 chromosomes, and, since none have been added, the drone also has 16 chromosomes. The development of an egg without fertilization is known as *parthenogenesis.*

SIGNIFICANCE OF MITOTIC CELL DIVISION AND
MATURATION OF THE GERM CELLS

These processes suggest the following observations, which are important to the bee breeder:

1. The mitotic cell divisions, which take place in the developing bee, insure that all of the cells of the bee's body have the same kinds of chromosomes and in the same number. Since each chromosome pair carries particular genes, all of the body cells therefore have the same genes.

2. The reduction in the number of chromosomes from 32 to 16 during the maturation of the egg furnishes the mechanism whereby the fertilized eggs always have 32 chromosomes. The matured egg has 16 and the spermatozoon brings in 16 more to restore the number in the fertilized egg, or zygote, to 32.

3. The separation of the two members of each pair of homologous chromosomes during meiosis and the random way that they go into the nuclei make possible many different combinations of chromosomes in the pronuclei of the eggs.

4. Since the drones develop from unfertilized eggs which are *gametes,* the drones are, from a genetic viewpoint, actually gametes, and strictly speaking are not another generation.

5. There is no reduction division in the maturation of the male germ cells, and all of the spermatozoa have exactly the same kinds of genes. The spermatozoa of the drone therefore represent a particular gamete of the mother multiplied millions of times.

6. When a queen mates with a single drone, all of the spermatozoa which are stored in her spermatheca are alike, and the genetic variations exhibited by her worker progeny are due to the different kinds of gametes which she produces.

7. The genetic variations exhibited by the drones of a queen are also due to the different kinds of gametes the queen produces.

Some Fundamental Principles of Inheritance

Every honey bee fundamentally resembles every other honey bee. All have basically similar body structures. Within races, more specific resemblances are found. Caucasian bees resemble other Caucasian bees; all Italians have a yellow abdominal marking. The tendency of succeeding generations to resemble the preceding ones is termed *heredity*. But similarity is *not* total. Italian bees differ in coloration among themselves as well as from the markings of Caucasians. These and other differences are *variations*. The study of inheritance in the honey bee is complicated by the wide differences in appearances and functions of the three castes, and by the difficulty in recognizing the same character in the queen, the drone, and the worker.

The normal eye color in bees is black, but occasionally drones with white eyes appear in a colony of black-eyed bees. The abdominal markings of the drones may also vary and other physical variations may appear. The black eyes, the white eyes, and the abdominal markings are *characters*. The black eyes belong to the same *morphological feature*, eye color, as white eyes, but the two eye colors develop in opposing directions and are spoken of as *contrasting characters*. Black eyes and yellow body color are not contrasting characters; they belong to different morphological features. Characters may be tangible, discernible physical attributes, such as eye colors, or they may be physiological and intangible in nature, such as temper or oviposition rate.

Characters are the end products of the development of the bee from germ cell to adult. Characters result from the action of the *environment* upon determining *factors* in the cells which were transmitted from the parents to the offspring in the germ cells.

The factors are functionally discrete particles, also known as *genes*. The genes are located in the chromosomes, arranged one beside the other like beads on a string. Each gene occupies a particular position in a particular chromosome; this position is the gene *locus*. The mate of the chromosome has the same or similar genes at corresponding loci. The two genes of a particular locus of a chromosome pair are often called a *gene pair*.

The two genes which occupy corresponding loci of chromosome mates may be somewhat different, but both affect the same body structure or other feature. For instance, each gene which causes white eye in the bee differs from its mate which produces black eye, but both are at the same locus. These differing but similar genes of a particular locus are known as *alleles;* one is said to be *allelic* to the other. The white eye gene at a particular locus is thus an allele of the black eye gene at the same locus. Genes affecting a given feature are not necessarily allelic. The four known genes which produce white eyes, for example, are at different loci and are non-allelic to each other.

When the two alleles are present in the cells, one of them often appears to have a stronger influence on the trait they both affect. Thus, when the cells of the bee have both a black eye gene and a white eye gene, the bees' eyes are black. The black eye gene is said to have *dominance,* for it "dominates" the white eye gene, the *recessive* gene. Only when both genes of a pair are recessive does a recessive character develop. Thus, when two white eye allelic genes are present in the cells of female bees, the bees have white eyes; but when one gene is white eye and the other black eye, the bees have black eyes.

When the two genes of a gene pair in the female bee are alike, they are said to be in *homozygous* condition, and the bee is homozygous for the character produced by the genes. The bee then must breed "true" for the particular character, for all germ cells it produces have the same gene for the character. But when the two genes of a pair are unlike (in *heterozygous* condition), the bee does not breed true for the character; half of the gametes receive each kind of gene.

Drones, having only one set of chromosomes, have only one of the genes of a gene pair. At a particular locus, a drone may have a black eye gene or a white eye gene, but not both. The single gene determines the character. The drone, the male bee, is in effect homozygous for all genes. And all spermatozoa produced by a particular drone must also have identical genes. Such haploid individuals are said to be *hemizygous.* The genes of a drone may also be considered to be completely *sex-linked.*

As mentioned previously, the normal eye color of bees is black, but sometimes a drone is found with eyes which are white, or chartreuse, or red; or there may be no eyes at all. These deviations from normal are frequently heritable and usually arise through a change in a normal gene, or one of its alleles. When a gene changes and the resultant gene produces an effect on a trait different from the effect produced by the original gene, the change is called mutation. Usually the mutant gene is recessive to the normal gene.

When more than one kind of gene arises at a particular locus by mutation, there are more than two alleles though only two can be in a cell at the same time, and an individual female bee can have only two of them, and a drone only one of them. In these cases the normal gene and the mutant genes form a series of alleles which are called *multiple alleles.* This is illustrated by the allelic series at the chartreuse locus in bees: ch^+ (normal black), ch^1 (chartreuse-1), ch^2 (chartreuse-2), ch^c (cherry), and ch^r (red).

The two alleles, the normal one for black eye and the mutant one for white eye, exist together in the same cells of a queen heterozygous for them. The black eye gene is dominant over the white eye gene, and the queen has black eyes. But the black eye gene does not affect the white eye gene itself. Alleles affect only the characters, not each other. When the eye color alleles separate at meiosis, during the maturation of the egg, one remains in the egg pronucleus and the other is eliminated in the polar body. It is a matter of chance which of the two eye color genes remains in the egg pronucleus after the meiotic divisions are finished, but on the average each allele will get into the pronucleus an equal number of times. Thus, approximately half of the eggs will have the black and approximately half the white eye allele. If these eggs are unfertilized, they will develop into drones in the ratio of about one black-eyed drone to one white-eyed drone. The separation of the alleles at meiosis and their distribution to different gametes, where each may again assert its effect on a character, is called *segregation*. Segregation is a constant feature of all diploid inheritance.

The genes on homologous chromosomes segregate and are distributed to germ cells independently of genes on other chromosomes. This can be illustrated by an example. If alleles W and w, which affect eye color, are carried on one chromosome pair, and alleles B and b, which affect some other trait, are carried on another chromosome pair, W and w will separate and go into gametes independently of the separation and distribution of B and b. Half of the gametes will have W and half w; half will also have B and half b. But it is a matter of chance whether W and B or W and b go into the same gamete, and both combinations occur an equal number of times. Likewise gametes which have w may get B or b, and these combinations also occur with equal frequency. Thus four types of gametes are formed in equal numbers: WB, Wb, wB, and wb. The segregation and independent entrance of the genes into these combinations is called *independent assortment*, one of the fundamental principles of heredity.

Each chromosome of a cell has many genes, each of which exerts a more or less pronounced effect upon respective traits. The gene for black eye, for instance, may be on the same chromosome as a dominant gene affecting some unrelated character. Since the two genes are on the *same chromosome,* they tend to stay together when the gametes are formed and are said to be *linked*. When homologous chromosomes come together at meiosis, they exchange segments, as *crossing over,* and a certain percentage of the time the point of exchange occurs between these two particular linked genes. They thus become separated and go into different gametes in which they have new linkage relationships which are retained until crossing over again takes place.

The genes of an organism make up the *genotype;* the characters due to these genes make up the *phenotype.* The geneticist often works with only a few genes at a time, which he selects to represent the genotype, and ignores the rest of the genes.

Inheritance of White Eye Color

Some of the principles discussed above can be illustrated by considering the inheritance of white eye color in the honeybee. Some black-eyed queens produce black-eyed workers but drones of which half have black eyes and half white eyes. If the white-eyed drones are mated to their black-eyed sisters, half of the latter produce black-eyed workers and white-eyed workers in about equal proportions as well as black-eyed and white-eyed drones in approximately equal proportions. The other half of the sisters produce only black-eyed workers and black-eyed drones.

Since the first-generation queen produces both black-eyed and white-eyed drones, she must be heterozygous for the eye color factors. These factors are often designated by the initial letters of the names of the mutant genes. Thus in the case of white eye color in the bee, the recessive gene, white eye, is represented by small *w,* and the dominant gene, black eye, by large *W.* The genotype and phenotype of the queen and her offspring are shown in the diagram on the facing page.

The chart shows that the parent queen possessed a factor for black eye color and a factor for white eye color, being heterozygous in respect to this factor pair. She was black eyed herself, showing the black eye factor was dominant. The queen produced two kinds of eggs in equal numbers, which may be represented by any multiple of 2. In this case, four eggs are represented, two of which are not fertilized and develop into drones, and two of which are fertilized and develop into workers. One egg of each group has the white and the other egg the black eye factor. All of the spermatozoa of the drones to which the queen was mated are alike; since the drones had black eyes, all of their spermatozoa have the black eye factor. Thus the fertilized eggs all receive a black eye factor from the spermatozoa, and the resulting workers all have black eyes.

The result of mating white-eyed drones to their heterozygous sisters is shown by the diagram. Both the female and the male progeny of a

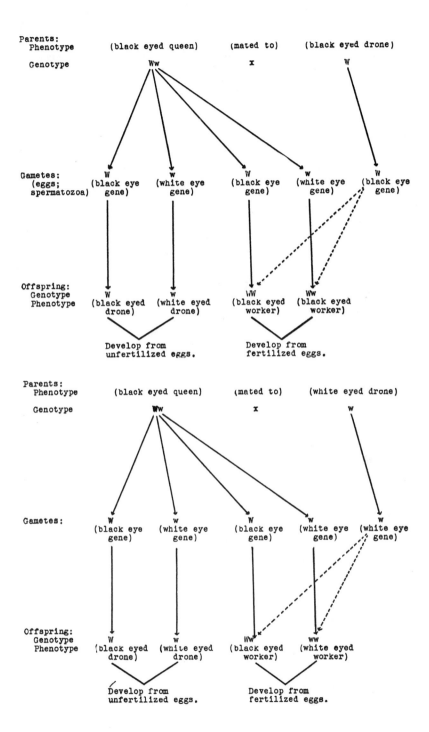

Parents:
  Phenotype   (black eyed queen)   (mated to)   (black eyed drone)

  Genotype   Ww   x   W

Gametes:
  (eggs;   W   w   W   w   W
  spermatozoa) (black eye   (white eye   (black eye   (white eye   (black eye
                 gene)   gene)   gene)   gene)   gene)

Offspring:
  Genotype   W   w   WW   Ww
  Phenotype   (black eyed   (white eyed   (black eyed   (black eyed
                 drone)   drone)   worker)   worker)

                      Develop from   Develop from
                      unfertilized eggs.   fertilized eggs.

Parents:
  Phenotype   (black eyed queen)   (mated to)   (white eyed drone)

  Genotype   Ww   x   w

Gametes: W   w   W   w   w
                (black eye   (white eye   (black eye   (white eye   (white eye
                 gene)   gene)   gene)   gene)   gene)

Offspring:
  Genotype   W   w   Ww   ww
  Phenotype   (black eyed   (white eyed   (black eyed   (white eyed
                 drone)   drone)   worker)   worker)

                      Develop from   Develop from
                      unfertilized eggs.   fertilized eggs.

heterozygous black-eyed queen mated to white-eyed drones occur in the proportion of about half white-eyed and half black-eyed.

Breeding Methods

The goal in bee breeding is to concentrate and intensify desirable characters in a strain or line and at the same time eliminate the undesirable ones. Since characters are expressions of their genes, this means concentrating in a line a maximum number of genes which contribute toward the desired characters.

In beginning a stock improvement program, the bee breeder must decide which characters are the most important, and must confine his efforts to these. It is relatively easy to establish one character in a line if the character is dependent upon a single gene pair. But as more characters are combined, the problem rapidly becomes more complex. It becomes especially difficult when the various characters are influenced by several gene pairs and multiple alleles.

The most important economic consideration in dealing with honey bees is large per colony honey yield. The honey yield is a composite of several characters. It depends upon colony population and industry. Colony population depends upon oviposition rate, brood viability, and longevity of the workers. Among other characters to be considered are resistance to diseases, gentleness, and non-swarming tendency.

Characters may conveniently be classified into two general types: those which either are fully developed or do not appear at all, and those which appear in varying degrees. Eye color illustrates the first type. The yellow coloring of the abdomen illustrates the second type. Characters which vary in amount or degree are *quantitative characters;* those which are either fully present or absent are *qualitative characters.* Most of the economically important characters of the bee are quantitative. Some of these may be measured, such as oviposition rate or longevity, but others, such as temper, are difficult to measure and an estimate of them can probably best be made by repeated observations.

The expression of qualitative characters is often governed by one gene or pair of genes. This is the situation in the inheritance and expression of white eye color in the bee. Here one of the alleles is dominant over the other. In some cases, neither gene may be dominant, but the two alleles may produce an effect intermediate between the two extremes. In still other cases the dominant allele of any one of two or more factor pairs may produce a particular character. For instance, if two gene pairs such as *Aa* and *Bb* have the same effect on a character, the character will appear fully developed even if only one dominant is present, as *Aabb,* or *aaBb.* If no dominants are present, as *aabb,* the opposite or contrasting character is produced.

Quantitative characters are dependent upon more than one pair of genes and are more susceptible to environmental influences than are qualitative characters. Quantitative genes, also called *multiple factors,* exhibit a cumulative effect so that two similar genes from the same gene pair or from different gene pairs for a particular character produce a greater effect than one gene. Thus a bee with one gene for yellow, *Yyy'y'*, has less yellow than one with two genes for yellow, *YYy'y'* or *YyY'y'*, which in turn has less yellow than a bee with three genes for yellow, *YYY'y'*.

Most of the economically important characters of bees are probably dependent upon several gene pairs. Since the degree of development of a quantitative character is governed by the number of contributing genes present, one of the first steps in bee breeding is to bring these genes together into one line. Any particular colony or line will probably have only some of the desirable genes. Thus the problem of concentrating the desired genes in a line may entail bringing the genes together from several lines by crossing the lines. Then, by inbreeding and selection the bee breeder endeavors to hold the desired genes together in the same individuals. Undesirable genes may accompany the desirable ones, however, and they must be eliminated.

Inbreeding involves the mating together of individuals more closely related than the average of the group, line, or strain. There are different degrees of inbreeding. The more closely related the mated individuals are, the more inbred their progeny will be. The most intensive inbreeding is self-fertilization, which is possible with bees because a virgin queen can be stimulated to lay eggs which will develop into drones with which she can then be mated. Self-fertilization is very rare among other animals. The next most intensive inbreeding is brother-sister mating which in the bee is parent-offspring mating.

The purpose of inbreeding is to put the gene pairs in homozygous condition and to keep particular genes in the line. It tends to achieve this because the genes which the progeny receive come from common ancestors and are therefore more likely to be identical genes than if they came from different ancestors. Inbreeding sorts the genes, breaks up old combinations and makes new ones, and brings undesirable genes to light. The breeder must select and attempt to hold these genes by choosing the right individuals for mating together.

As inbreeding progresses, the bees may become less industrious, a greater proportion of the eggs and larvae may die, and other undesirable conditions may appear. These occur, in part at least, because some of the desirable genes become separated from the others at meiosis and get into different gametes and then into different bees. They become lost as the line is carried on because the bee breeder cannot use every kind of individual as breeding stock. The loci of these desirable genes are then occupied by their recessive alleles, and the less desirable characters produced by the recessives appear.

These undesirable effects are to be expected; but at the same time all of the genes tend to become homozygous. After the genes are homozygous they are not lost because when the genes of a given pair separate at meiosis an identical gene goes into each daughter nucleus and all of the gametes have the gene. Genes which are in heterozygous condition may be lost because the undesirable gene may get into the bee selected to continue the line.

After several generations of inbreeding and selection, the inbred lines may be crossed to combine their desired genes. The queens from these crosses may then be mated to drones from other inbred lines. These queens and their progeny should be quite uniform in appearance and performance. The performances will probably vary according to which lines are crossed, but should generally be superior.

Inbred lines which cross well may be maintained for crossing, or inbreeding may be reinitiated from the queens which were hybrids between the lines. The process of selection and inbreeding is then repeated.

The system of mating which is employed will depend upon the immediate objective of the mating and may vary with each generation. Three types of matings are illustrated below in *path* (or *arrow*) *diagrams*. The eggs or female parents are indicated by solid arrows, and the spermatozoa, or male parents, by broken arrows. The male parents are not themselves shown in the diagram because they are genetically gametes of their mothers, who are shown.

PARENT-OFFSPRING

Queen number one (Q1) is mated to a drone of queen number two (Q2) to produce queen number three (Q3). Queen number three (Q3)

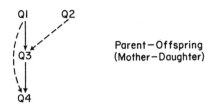

Parent—Offspring
(Mother—Daughter)

is mated to a drone of her mother (her brother) to produce queen number four (Q4). This is not a brother-sister mating as it appears to be but is a parent-offspring mating, for the eggs or gametes of Q3 are fertilized by the spermatozoa of a son of her mother, Q1, which are identical to the gamete from which the drone arose. Thus Q1 has the genetic role of both mother and father.

SIBLING

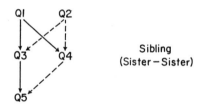

Sibling
(Sister—Sister)

Sibling matings are ordinarily the matings of full brother and sister. It is impossible to make full brother-sister matings in the bee, but full sister-sister matings can be made by mating virgins to their sister's drones. If Q1 is mated with *one* drone of Q2, the daughters, Q3 and Q4, will be more closely related than is ordinarily the case between sisters, inasmuch as the spermatozoa fertilizing the eggs producing Q3 and Q4 are identical. Usually the spermatozoa which fertilize the female germ cells in other organisms are different, for a diploid individual produces many kinds of germ cells; this condition would be approached if Q1 were mated to several drones of Q2.

COUSIN

The mating of single first cousins, as diagramed on page 132, does not constitute intensive inbreeding.

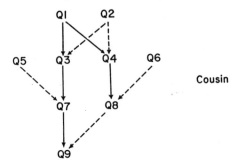

The genetics and breeding of any organism require study and careful observations. The breeding of the honey bee has its own peculiar difficulties and its own advantages. There is no easy way to produce a better bee. The discussions in this chapter have little more than touched on the principles of genetics and breeding, and the bee breeder would do well to study at least one or more of the standard genetics textbooks.[2,3]

A Suggested Breeding Program for the Commercial Beekeeper

The beekeeper would like, of course, a simple way to improve his stock. He no doubt would prefer to have little or nothing to do with chromosomes, genes, and the relationships of his queens. Unfortunately, there is no simple formula for bee breeding which will always work and which will entail little effort on the part of the beekeeper. If there were, there would be no need for the employment of geneticists and for the expenditure of large sums of money on breeding projects.

But the beekeeper *can* improve his stock, even though he may know little about animal breeding, if he is willing to make the effort which is required. The beekeeper must be willing to make careful observations on each colony under test and must provide an abundance of selected drones to insure that a good proportion of his queens are mated with the desired stock.

[2] Sinnott, Edmund W., L. C. Dunn, and Th. Dobzhansky. 1950. Principles of Genetics. 505 pp. McGraw-Hill Book Company, Inc., New York.

[3] Lush, L. L. 1945. Animal Breeding Plans, 439 pp. Iowa State College Press, Ames.

A colony of bees consists of two generations: the queen, the mother of the colony, and the workers, offspring of the queen. In judging a colony, the performances of both generations must be evaluated. The queen is judged by the quantity of brood she produces and whether she misses many cells when she lays eggs (Fig. 57). A good queen will lay 1200 or more eggs each 24 hours during the intensive brood-rearing period. She will not ordinarily have more than three to five empty cells per hundred among the sealed brood of the better combs. She will lay to the bottom of the combs and as far to the sides and top as the stores of pollen and honey permit (Fig. 58). During the initial period of expansion of the brood nest, she will lay as many eggs as the bees can possibly care for, and often she seems to lay more than they can care for. She will maintain a high egg-laying rate until forced to reduce it by lack of room or until the bees change her diet. The purity of the queen's own breeding is indicated by the evenness of the color of her drones, as well as by her own appearance.

The bees are judged by their longevity, nectar gathering ability, temper, willingness to enter supers and draw foundation, tendency to swarm, resistance to diseases, and other characteristics. Their purity of breeding is indicated by the evenness of their abdominal markings.

The beekeeper can approach his breeding problem in several ways. Most commonly, he selects as breeders one or more colonies which

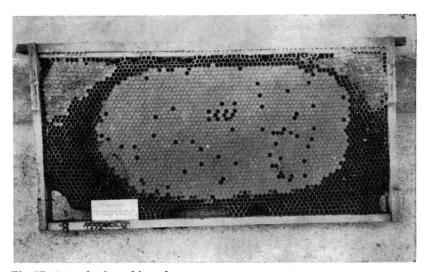

Fig. 57. A comb of good brood.

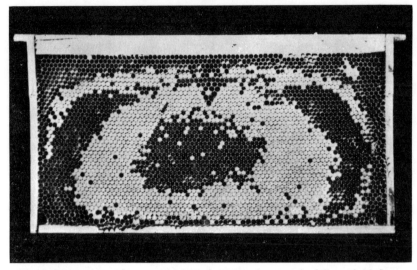

Fig. 58. Emergence pattern of brood where the eggs had been laid first at the center of the comb and then in rings to the comb edges.

have made the most honey during the season and which have fairly evenly marked bees. The entire outfit is then requeened from these breeders and new breeders are selected the following year or the year after. This system can work very well to maintain good stock or to replace poor stock with good, but improvement in the better stock is very slow. Several dangers, which often are not recognized, are associated with this system. If, for example, one favorite breeder is used to requeen a large proportion of the colonies and the following year is again used extensively, her daughters will, in many cases, mate with drones from her daughters of the first year, and this may result in many of these younger daughters producing "spotted" brood, that is, many empty cells among the sealed brood. This can be remedied, and the original stock characteristics retained, by using a breeder from another good stock as a queen mother, mating her daughters to the original stock. Two generations of this kind of mating should recover the desired characteristics of the original stock.

Perhaps a better method would be to select several outstanding queens and requeen the producing colonies with their daughters, then selecting as the basic breeding stock the three of these breeders *whose daughters* produced the best brood and headed colonies which produced the most honey. A letter, number, or name should be given each breeder to identify her, and then a systematic program of breeding should be started.

Let us say the three selected breeders have been designated A, B, and C. Full frames of drone comb should be put into their colonies as early in the spring as is feasible, and as soon as the drone cells are sealed the drone brood should be removed and put into other drone-free colonies, one colony for each breeder queen. These colonies should preferably be queenless. A new drone comb should then be given each breeder. The breeder colonies should be kept producing drones in large numbers as long as drones are needed. The production of drones may be encouraged by feeding the breeder colonies with honey or sugar syrup, and with pollen.

The drone nursery colonies should be located in an area as isolated as possible both from other bees and from each other. They should soon have large numbers of drones. There should be one colony with drones from breeder A; its location might be called "queenyard A." There should be drone nursery colonies with drones from breeders B and C located in their respective yards. These colonies must be maintained by the frequent addition of brood, and all drone brood in the frames of added brood should be destroyed.

Queens should be reared from the three breeder queens. The first year, A's queens should be put into nuclei and the queens mated in queenyard B. B's queens should be mated in queenyard C, and C's queens should be mated in queenyard A. These queens should be used to requeen honey producing colonies, and should be tested during the season. The best queen of *each breeder,* designated respectively as A′, B′, and C′, should then be selected as mothers of the next generation of queens.

The next year the queens from A^1 should be mated to drones of C^1, queens of B^1 should be mated to drones of A^1, and queens of C^1 should be mated to drones of B^1. These young queens should be tested as before, and the best queen of each line should be selected as a new breeder and should be given a designation. The following year the system of mating followed the first year should be used: the queens from A^2 should be mated to drones from B^2, the queens from B^2 should be mated to drones of C^2, and queens from C^2 should be mated to drones of A^2. In succeeding years the two systems of mating are continually alternated, and the best queen of each line being selected annually for the new breeder. The matings to be made are shown in table 4.

TABLE 4. SYSTEM OF MATING

Queens from	Mated to drones from			
	1st year	*2nd year*	*3rd year*	*4th year*
A line	B	C^1	B^2	C^3
B line	C	A^1	C^2	A^3
C line	A	B^1	A^2	B^3

The selection of breeder queens from each generation is a critical part of a breeding program. Any progress to be made in improving the stock will depend largely on these selections. Records should be kept for each colony under test. They should include observations on the amount of surplus honey produced by the colony, swarming tendency, gentleness of the bees, their quietness on the combs, solidness of the brood, quantity of the brood, resistance to sac brood and, as far as practicable, to other diseases, and willingness of the bees to draw foundation. Evenness of abdominal markings is not too important at first, although a standard should be established towards which to work. The best colonies which also have color markings closest to the goal should be chosen as breeding colonies. After several generations of careful selection, the color markings of the queens, bees, and drones should become quite uniform.

It is wise to test the performances of potential breeder queens for two years if possible. It is also wise to test their daughters in producing colonies. The queens which are best on both counts—demonstrated performance and demonstrated ability to pass their good qualities to their offspring—are chosen as breeders.

The testing of potential breeding stock is subject to many errors which must be guarded against. Drifting of the worker bees is one of the most serious. Colonies under test should be located so that drifting is reduced to a minimum. Colonies should not be arranged in even rows nor bunched together. They should be located several feet apart and with natural markers for each colony.

Differences in the starting strength of the colonies and variations in colony management may introduce errors. All colonies under test should either be placed in one yard or representative colonies from each line should be distributed among several testing yards. Locations vary even within short distances and location differences must be taken into account in evaluating the stocks.

CHAPTER VII

Controlled Mating

THE FEMALE HONEY BEE develops from a fertilized egg in which half of the hereditary factors is supplied by the mother through the egg nucleus and half by the father through the spermatozoon which unites with the egg nucleus. The male honey bee develops from an unfertilized egg and receives all of his hereditary factors from his mother, but she in turn received half of her factors from her mother and half from her father. It is apparent therefore that, since half of the hereditary factors are passed on to succeeding generations through the male, the selection of the male parent is equally as important as the selection of the female parent if satisfactory progress in improving the honey bee is to be made.

The desire to control the mating of the queen is an old one. As early as 1740 Reaumur[1] confined a queen and some drones together in a glass dish, expecting to witness the mating of the queen. This experiment failed as have others of a like nature since that time. Apparently the first person to try to inseminate a queen artificially was Huber,[2] but he failed in his attempt. In the years that followed, almost every conceivable way to inseminate the queen or otherwise control her mating was tried. These attempts were attended with failure or, at best, with indifferent success.

Isolated mating stations have been employed with satisfactory results in some European countries since early in the twentieth century.[3,4] Their usefulness in this country is limited by the difficulty of finding suitable and sufficiently isolated areas.

---

[1] Reaumur, R. A. F. 1740. Memoires pour sevir à l'histoire des insects. Paris.
[2] Huber, Francis. 1814. New observations upon bees. Transl. by C. P. Dadant. American Bee Journal, Hamilton, Illinois.
[3] Brunnich, Dr. 1913. Fertilizing queens at a mating station. Gl. Bee Cult. 41(14): 493–7.
[4] Heberle, J. A. 1913. Mating stations. Gl. Bee Cult. 41(14):497–8.

It appears that the most feasible way to control the male parentage is to inseminate queens artificially with spermatozoa from selected drones. The technique of artificial insemination has been developed during the past three decades to the point of practicability in breeding work. In spite of the advances made in techniques and instruments, however, the artificial insemination of queens requires considerable skill, which can be acquired only with much practice; and costly apparatus is necessary for the operation.

Techniques and Instruments

Up to the present time, nearly all workers on the artificial insemination of queen bees have concentrated on the problem of getting the semen into the reproductive system of the queen. It was shown in 1911 [5] that the semen is deposited in the oviducts at natural mating; this fact was verified by other work in 1917 [6] and again in 1920 [7] and 1944.[8] When a queen mates naturally, the semen is deposited in the vagina, median oviduct, and the lateral oviducts, and the spermatozoa migrate to the spermatheca over a period of several hours. The filled spermatheca contains 5,000,000 or more spermatozoa, which live in the spermatheca for the life of the queen but do not increase in number there. A few spermatozoa are withdrawn by the queen each time an egg which is to be fertilized is laid. After many eggs have been laid, the supply of spermatozoa may be so reduced that the queen becomes a partial drone layer. A queen with fewer than 5,000,000 spermatozoa in the spermatheca might be considered to be partially inseminated.

Mature drones can be made to evert the copulatory organ, or penis, and ejaculate the seminal fluids by the application of pressure to the abdomen, by decapitation, or other stimuli. The most obvious method to inseminate the queen would be to bring the drone into juxtaposition with her and then, by pressure on the drone's abdomen, cause the copulatory organ to evert into the sting chamber and vagina of the queen, with consequent injection of the seminal fluids into the ovi-

---

[5] Zander, Enoch. 1911. Der Bau der Biene. Verlagbuchhandlung, Eugen Ulmer. Stuttgart.

[6] Shafer, Geo. D. 1917. A study of the factors which govern mating in the honeybee. Mich. Ag. Col. Exp. Sta. Tech. Bul. 34.

[7] Bishop, Geo. H. 1920. Fertilization of the honeybee. I. Disposal of the sexual fluids in the organs of the female. Jour. Exp. Zool. 31(2):225–65, 267–86.

[8] Laidlaw, Harry H. Jr., 1944. Artificial insemination of the queen bee (*Apis mellifera* L.): Morphological basis and results. Jour. Morph. 74(3):426–65.

ducts. This method was tried by many workers with only meager success.

One of the later methods of using the copulatory organ to transfer the semen involved a modification of this procedure, causing only a partial eversion of the end of the organ before its insertion into the vagina, after which eversion was completed by further pressure on the drone's abdomen. The end of the organ was severed from the drone and left in the queen as a plug to retain the semen in the reproductive tract. Ejaculation of the seminal fluids had taken place almost simultaneously with the partial eversion of the copulatory organ, and the semen was caught and retained in the organ bulb. When further eversion was brought about, the semen was released from the bulb when it reached the end of the everting penis and, with the penis in the vagina or pressed against it, the semen was deposited there.

This method gave quite consistently slight inseminations. It was later discovered that the valvefold prevented the passage of the semen from the vagina into the oviducts, and this was responsible, in part at least, for the partial inseminations. The vagina was usually filled with semen, and since it can contain only a small part of the semen of a normal drone, insufficient for a complete insemination, the remainder was forced into the bursa copulatrix and its pouches. It should be mentioned that either the seminal vesicles or the bulb of the partially everted penis can be used to inject the semen contained in them into the oviducts of the queen if the valvefold is lowered.

The microsyringe, as devised by Watson and demonstrated in 1926,[9] afforded an easier method for injecting the semen into the reproductive tract of the queen. Syringes of various types had been used by workers prior to Watson, but with only occasional success. Watson's syringe was constructed of glass, with a plunger extending into a capillary tip. The plunger was moved by a screw mechanism which gave positive control of its action. This syringe was very efficient and it or some modification of it has been used by most workers since 1926. Recently syringes have been constructed with removable glass or plastic tips, which do not have the plunger in the tip. These have superseded the original Watson type and other syringes because of the greater sturdiness and convenience of the movable tip and the elimination of the problem of wear caused by the plunger.

Watson and his followers experienced the same difficulty in getting

---

[9] Cale, G. H. 1926. The first successful attempt to control the mating of queen bees. Amer. Bee Jour. 66(11):533–34.

the semen into the oviducts as had other workers, and their queens were also, for the most part, only partially inseminated even after several injections.[10,11] In 1933 it was discovered that the fold in the vagina, called the valvefold, prevented the passage of the injected semen into the oviducts, and that when this fold was lowered with a probe, injection of semen beyond it was possible.[8] It had been found three years earlier that queens anaesthetized with carbon dioxide or ether were easier to inseminate than those which were active during the operation.[10] Recent studies[11] have disclosed that queens subjected to carbon dioxide for two ten-minute periods are often stimulated to lay whether inseminated or not.

The injection of the semen into the queen is a delicate operation. The organs of the queen are so small (the vaginal orifice is about 0.66 mm. in diameter) that positive control of all movements is essential. Watson[12] tied the queen in a tilted cradle which he fastened to the microscope stage, and clamped the syringe in a Barber pipette manipulator fastened to the right edge of the stage. The manipulator held the syringe in line with the longitudinal axis of the queen and provided smooth positive movement of the syringe in all directions. The sting chamber of the queen was opened with forceps held in the operator's left hand and the syringe was inserted into the vagina by adjusting the manipulator with the right hand. Had not the valvefold interfered with passage of the semen into the oviducts, this technique and these instruments would have been quite satisfactory for a skilled operator.

Other workers have subsequently developed apparatus and techniques of their own. Two of the instruments which were devised have undergone a somewhat convergent evolution, and although they operate on much the same principle they differ considerably in construction. One of these,[13,14] developed by Nolan and refined and improved by Roberts and Mackensen (Figs. 59, 60), consists of a heavy metal false stage which is made to lie transversely across, but unattached to,

---

[10] Laidlaw, Harry H. Jr., 1949. Development of precision instruments for artificial insemination of queen bees. Jour. Econ. Ent. 42(2):254–61.

[11] Mackensen, Otto. 1947. Effect of carbon dioxide on initial oviposition of artificially inseminated and virgin queens. Jour. Econ. Ent. 40(3):344–9.

[12] Watson, Lloyd R. 1927. Controlled mating of queen bees. 50 pp. Amer. Bee Jour.

[13] Nolan, W. J. 1932. Breeding the honeybee under controlled conditions. U.S.D.A. Tech. Bul. 326.

[14] Anonymous. Roberts and Mackensen apparatus for artificial insemination of queen bees. Amer. Bee Jour. 87(9):425.

Fig. 59. Roberts and Mackensen insemination apparatus. (Photograph courtesy of U.S.D.A. and University of Wisconsin.)

the stage of a dissecting microscope. It is fitted near both ends with metal posts which carry a metal bar between them bearing the queen confined in a plastic tube with the terminal abdominal segments protruding. The tube is provided with a stopper and with tubing for administering carbon dioxide to the queen. Above the bar, each post is fitted with an adjustable metal block having a hole through which the handle of a modified teasing needle is inserted and in which it can slide. The needles are used to open the sting chamber and one is fashioned to fit beneath the sting and pull it from over the vaginal orifice. The syringe is held by an adjustable metal block secured to the tip of the post on the right side (for right-hand operation). Movement of the syringe for insertion into the vagina is accomplished by sliding the syringe through the hole in the supporting block. The valvefold is held from over the orifice of the median oviduct with a probe while the end of the syringe is inserted into the median oviduct.

The second instrument was developed by Laidlaw. It consists of a

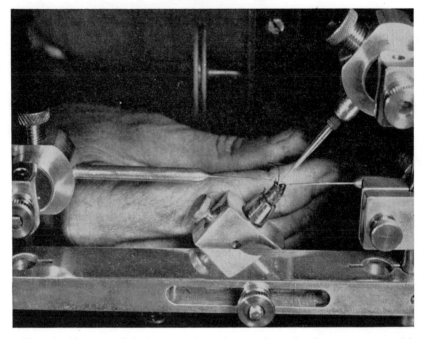

Fig. 60. Close-up of Roberts and Mackensen insemination apparatus with queen. (Photograph courtesy of U.S.D.A. and University of Wisconsin.)

queen manipulator and a syringe manipulator (Fig. 61). The queen manipulator weighs about three pounds, and is six inches long and three and one-quarter inches high, a convenient size to fit on the stage of a dissecting microscope. The anaesthetization chamber is situated at the middle of the instrument and clamps the queen's thorax firmly while allowing the abdomen to extend above the chamber (Fig. 62). The carbon dioxide used as an anaesthetic is directed from either side toward the thoracic spiracles. The opening hooks, one of which fits beneath the sting, are held by chucks fastened to pieces movable up or down and toward or away from the queen by means of racks and pinions. The queen can be tilted to any desired angle by means of a ball-and-socket joint. The manipulator, with the queen in place, can be removed from the stage while the syringe is being filled, and then the queen can be brought into proper position for insertion of the syringe into the vagina by sliding the queen manipulator over the stage of the microscope.

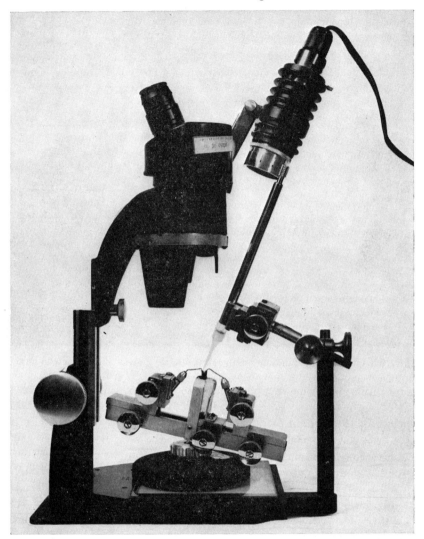

Fig. 61. Laidlaw queen bee insemination manipulators (Mackensen syringe).

The syringe manipulator is fastened by a bar and adjustable rod to a plate upon which the microscope rests. The bar fits against the front part of the microscope stage. The syringe is held firmly by a clamp which permits its ready removal and which will take any type syringe. The syringe can be raised or lowered by a sliding piece with a rack

Fig. 62. Close-up of Laidlaw manipulator with queen (Mackensen syringe).

and pinion adjustment. Light is directed into the queen from a lamp fitted with heat-absorbing glass. The valvefold is held from over the orifice of the median oviduct with a valvefold lifter while the end of the syringe is inserted into the vagina.

The Roberts and Mackensen instruments can be purchased, or a wood and metal copy can be made by the beekeeper from directions given in *A Manual for the Artificial Insemination of Queen Bees* by Otto Mackensen and W. C. Roberts of the U.S.D.A. Division of Bee Culture. The Laidlaw instruments can be constructed from drawings available from him.

The procedures in using these instruments are similar. Complete directions for using the Roberts and Mackensen apparatus are given in the manual. Briefly, the queen is confined in the holding tube, with the last three abdominal segments protruding from the constricted end, and carbon dioxide, conducted from a CO_2 cylinder to the queen holder by a rubber tube, is allowed to flow gently over the queen. The holder with the queen is placed in its mounting block and is tilted toward the syringe at a 30° angle. The opening hooks are now put in position, with the dorsal hook fitted in the triangular area between the bases of the sting lancets, but the sting chamber is not opened wide at this time. The queen is left there while the syringe is filled.

The microscope is withdrawn slightly toward the operator to provide working space, and the syringe is placed in its holder. Eversion of the copulatory organ, which is accompanied by ejaculation of the seminal fluids, is brought about in a selected drone by exposing the drone to chloroform fumes. The eversion usually stops before the semen has been released to the exterior of the organ. Moderate pressure on the drone's abdomen will cause the organ to continue eversion and release the semen and accompanying mucus. The drone, with the everted organ and adhering fluids, is brought to the tip of the syringe and the semen is taken up into it. If more than one drone is used, this procedure is repeated until the desired amount of semen has been taken into the syringe. The syringe point is moistened to lubricate it and moved into position over the queen. The microscope is then pushed forward so the queen is in the field of vision and the opening hooks are adjusted so the sting chamber is opened wide to expose the vaginal opening. With a probe, the valvefold is pushed ventrally within the vagina, the point of the syringe is inserted into the median oviduct, and the probe is removed. The semen is then injected, slowly at first and then rapidly, after which the syringe is withdrawn from the queen and removed from its holder. The queen is then removed from the tube.

When the Laidlaw apparatus is used, the queen manipulator is placed to the left of the microscope, and the queen is anaesthetized with carbon dioxide while she is held in the hand or confined to a cage. She is then grasped by the abdomen between the thumb and forefinger of the left hand, and, with her ventral side toward the operator, her thorax is inserted into the anaesthetization chamber of the queen manipulator, care being taken to guide her midway between the sides of the chamber. She is clamped in this position between the sponge rubber facings of the chamber and the movable closing piece. The carbon dioxide gas flow is adjusted to a small stream, and the queen is left thus while the syringe is filled.

The Mackensen syringe used with these instruments is prepared by filling the end of the plastic syringe tip connector with distilled water or physiological saline solution containing an antibiotic, and the plastic syringe tip is screwed into place. By turning the syringe screw, part of the water or solution is forced from the tip, and the discharge is stopped when the fluid plunger will withdraw to the threads at the base of the tip when the screw is reversed. The fluid is again forced down the tip to within 3 mm. of the end, and the syringe, now ready for use, is clamped in the syringe manipulator.

A drone is selected and decapitated. If this does not initiate eversion, the abdomen is drawn lightly and quickly over a towel, or is squeezed with moderate pressure (do not mash) between the thumb and forefinger. Eversion may also be brought about by pushing the abdominal segments together. If the abdomen contracts under one of these stimuli, ejaculation has probably occurred. If it remains flaccid, ejaculation probably did not take place. If, as is usually the case, eversion stops short of full eversion, it is completed and the semen exposed by a forceful pressure on the contracted abdomen and the penis base. This method frequently separates the semen from the mucus. Too much pressure, however, may cause the penis to rupture, with consequent loss of the semen.

Absolutely no fecal matter from either the drone or queen should be taken into the syringe, and the semen should not be permitted to touch the drone's abdomen, wings, or legs. *Any contamination may result in the death of the queen.* If the tip needs to be cleaned on the outside, this should be done with clean facial tissue, never with the bare fingers. It is good practice to wash the hands whenever the tips are changed.

Six to ten cubic millimeters of semen are taken into the syringe for most inseminations, and at least six to ten drones are required. After the semen is taken from each drone, it is withdrawn one millimeter into the syringe tip to prevent drying. Some of the translucent mucus or watery bulb fluid may be taken up with or following the semen, but none of the white mucus should be included, for it will coagulate in the syringe and plug the median oviduct. After the syringe is filled, it is raised as far as the manipulator will take it, so that it will clear the queen and the manipulator hooks.

The queen manipulator with the queen is now brought to the microscope stage. The sting chamber is opened by fine forceps inserted into the sting chamber between the sting shaft and the sternum, and, while the sting chamber is held open, the sting shaft is pressed anteriorly with one leg of the forceps, turning the sting base to a better position for placing the sting hook. The sting hook is brought over the queen and is lowered into the sting chamber to the anterior wall. It is then moved dorsally and fitted between the bases of the sting lancets. The abdomen of the queen can be moved in any direction with the forceps to aid in fitting the sting hook. The ventral hook is now brought over the queen and lowered into the sting chamber, and the forceps are withdrawn. The ventral hook is adjusted, and then the sting hook so the sting is pulled from over the vaginal orifice and the anterior sting chamber wall is flat but not stretched.

The syringe is now lowered into the sting chamber and the queen manipulator is moved over the microscope stage until the end of the syringe tip is over the vaginal orifice or a little ventral to it. The syringe is then raised slightly and a flattened probe, the valvefold lifter, is inserted into the vagina (Fig. 63A). The ventral vaginal lip is pulled toward the sternum to open the vagina and expose the valvefold, and the probe is then pushed toward the sting until it goes beyond the end of the valvefold (Fig. 63B). At this point it is slipped under the valvefold (Fig. 63C) and the valvefold is *lifted* from over the orifice of the median oviduct (Fig. 63D). When properly done, the vagina appears as a moderately deep cavity and the orifice of the median oviduct can be seen as a slit. The valvefold is held *firmly* in this position while the syringe is inserted into the reproductive tract (Fig. 63E). Care must be taken not to catch the syringe on the dorsal

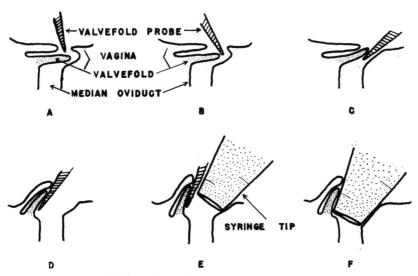

Fig. 63. Manner of lifting valvefold and inserting syringe.

edge of the vaginal orifice. The probe is now removed and the syringe tip pressed firmly against the reproductive opening *until* the surrounding tissues move with the syringe (Fig. 63F). The correctness of the position of the syringe is tested by a slight turning of the syringe screw. If semen moves down the syringe tip easily, then the tip is placed correctly. If not, the syringe is improperly placed or semen has dried in its tip. The semen is injected, and the syringe is raised and the fluid plunger run to the end of the tip to prevent semen from drying on the inner tip walls.

The hooks are now disengaged and moved up and away from the queen. The queen manipulator is again set aside and the queen is removed from the anaesthetization chamber. The tip of one wing is clipped to indicate she is artificially inseminated.

Syringe tips are sterilized after use by submergence overnight in strong sodium hypochlorite solution, and they are thoroughly flushed with distilled water the following day. It is imperative to keep the equipment clean, and especially the valvefold probe and the stage of the microscope. The valvefold probe is polished frequently with jewelers' rouge. No wax or other substance of any kind is permitted on the stage; a minute fleck of wax will interfere with the smooth movement of the queen manipulator over the stage.

Results

Queens which mate naturally receive semen from many drones. Usually, naturally mated queens receive a normal insemination. Mackensen and Roberts determined that the spermathecae of naturally mated queens contain an average of 5.73 million spermatozoa, ranging from 3.34 million to 7.35 million. Mature drones were found to have an average of about ten million spermatozoa in the seminal vesicles, more than enough to fully inseminate one queen. Their studies revealed further that the spermathecae of queens inseminated artificially with semen from one drone contained on the average 0.87 million spermatozoa, while the spermathecae of queens inseminated once with the semen from several drones (2.5 cubic millimeters of semen; the best drones had nearly 1 cubic millimeter of semen) contained an average of 2.97 million, and queens inseminated twice with semen from several drones received an average of 4.11 million spermatozoa in the spermatheca.

It is apparent from the above data that queens inseminated by present methods must receive semen from several drones if inseminations approaching the normal are to be obtained. Queens which are to maintain full colonies must have at least nearly normal inseminations. Queens inseminated at the University of California, Davis, have for many years been inseminated once with at least 5 cubic millimeters of semen, and it has been routine for several years to inject about 8 cubic millimeters. These queens have headed field colonies as successfully as naturally mated queens.

Naturally mated queens as a rule begin to lay about three days after mating, a few starting at two days and some at four days or longer. Artificially inseminated queens frequently do not begin laying until three weeks or more after they are inseminated. Queens inseminated by the writer often delay oviposition for an abnormal period, but a good proportion also lay fairly promptly. In one lot of 131 queens inseminated once in 1949, nine died of paralysis or other causes, 17 were given a second CO_2 treatment 3 to 17 days following insemination, after which they laid within two to five days, and 106 laid without further insemination or CO_2 treatment. Of these, five (4.1 per cent of the 122 queens which laid) began oviposition the second day following the insemination, 29 (23.8 per cent) laid at three days, and a total of 84 (68.5 per cent) were laying by the seventh day.

The discovery that carbon dioxide will cause the queen to lay has to a large extent solved the problem of delayed oviposition; nearly all queens given two treatments of CO_2 will lay within ten days, and very often much sooner. Why some inseminated queens lay promptly without a second CO_2 treatment and others do not, remains to be discovered, however.

Whether an inseminated queen will initially produce all worker brood or a mixture of worker and drone brood in worker cells appears to have little relation to the number of spermatozoa in the spermatheca, except that queens which have normal or nearly normal inseminations almost invariably produce all worker brood. There are many instances where queens which received few sperm in the spermatheca nevertheless produced all worker brood. In other instances, with spermathecae fairly well supplied with spermatozoa the queens were partial drone layers. The percentage of worker brood is thus an unreliable measure of the relative numbers of spermatozoa the queen possesses. Queens inseminated with 5 cubic millimeters or more of semen will usually be capable of maintaining a large colony for a season. Queens which receive considerably less than a normal insemination may become partial drone layers after a heavy and prolonged period of brood rearing.

Little is known of the physiological factors involved in the insemination of queen bees. There is evidence which indicates that drones must be well fed and cared for the first few days after their emergence if they are to mature large numbers of sperm. Drones may possibly differ not only in the quantity of semen, but also in the viability and activity of the spermatozoa. Drones matured in cages in cell-building colonies where they receive good care are ready for use when they are ten days old. Queens may be emerged in the nuclei they are to head, although queens emerged in cages, inseminated, and then introduced to nuclei perform equally as well. The emerging of queens in cages has a distinct advantage over emerging them in nuclei, and all queens artificially inseminated at Davis are now emerged by this method.

Care and Introduction of Inseminated Queens

Queenless nursery colonies[15] are used to emerge cells and care for virgin queens, to mature and care for drones, and to care for caged inseminated queens. They may be one or more stories high. The bodies contain nine frames so arranged there is a frame of honey and pollen next to each sidewall and one in the center. A frame of larvae occupies the third position from each side. This arrangement provides for four frames of caged queens or drones, one on each side of the combs of larvae. Package bees are added to make the colony strong, and new larvae and package bees are added each week. The colonies are fed continuously with sugar syrup, or by means of candy in a feeder board placed over the top of the hive like an inner cover.

Virgin queens and drones need no particular attention in the nursery colony, except that the bees should have access to the drones through an excluder on one side of the cage. Inseminated queens present a problem. The bees often show antagonism toward them, and unless the cages are properly constructed the queens may lose tarsi or segments of the antennae. It is not unusual for the bees to neglect some of the queens so that they starve. This can be avoided by putting several bees in the cage with the queen when she is returned to the nursery. This is a perfectly safe operation if bees which are *full of honey* are selected.

---

[15] Laidlaw, Harry H. Jr. 1958. Organization and operation of a bee breeding program. Proceedings Tenth International Congress of Entomology 4:1067–1078.

The inseminated queens are left in the nursery at least over night. They are introduced into five-frame nuclei in full bodies which have been made up in such a way that the older bees return to the parent colonies. A Boardman entrance feeder is placed on the bottom board of the nucleus in the space where the remaining frames will go later. It is provided with a quart jar of sugar syrup or diluted honey. Feeding is continuous until the queen begins to lay.

The queen is put into the nucleus in a Miller introducing cage or some modification of it, with enough attendant bees from the nucleus to crowd the cage, and the entrance to the nucleus is covered with queen excluder. When the queens lay, the excluders are removed from the nuclei and are replaced with robber screens.

It should be mentioned that absence of old bees and a *constant* supply of clean fresh syrup or diluted honey are essential to safe introduction of inseminated queens. The method described produced almost totally successful introductions at the University of California in 1960 and 1961.

CHAPTER VIII

The Ailments of Queen Bees

THE QUEEN BEE, although protected to some extent against chemical poisoning, is subject to the same diseases and ailments as workers and drones in both the brood and adult stages. The diseases of bees are discussed in detail in many of the textbooks on beekeeping,[1] and the various diseases, their symptoms and controls are mentioned here only as they relate to queen rearing.

Brood Diseases

FOULBROOD DISEASES

Queen larvae are subject to infection from the bacteria that affect the worker and drone larvae, but in many cases the symptoms are not so obvious in them because of the usually small number of queen larvae present in the hive at any one time. Larvae grafted from combs containing American or European foulbrood disease may be affected at the time of grafting yet have the appearance of healthy larvae. The result may be an apparently poor acceptance of the grafted cells since some of the larvae will be removed before the cells are sealed. This removal of the larvae by the bees generally occurs in the case of European foulbrood. When the larvae are infected with *Bacillus larvae,* the cause of American foulbrood, a majority of the larvae die after the cells are sealed, while the capped cells may appear to be perfectly healthy. Unless the cells are candled to reveal the condition of the

---

[1] Eckert, John E. and Frank R. Shaw. 1960. Beekeeping, Macmillan Company, 536 pp.

imago within, the infected cells may be introduced into nuclei and the dead larvae cause the infection of unsealed brood.

When any queen larvae are infected with either American or European foulbrood disease, its origin will be found in the colony from which the larvae were grafted or in the cell-building colony itself. Either disease can be prevented or eradicated by chemotherapy. In any event, either disease should be eradicated immediately and the contaminating colonies and equipment removed from the breeding program—unless disease resistance is being studied.

SACBROOD

The loss of larvae due to infection from sacbrood is of minor importance. However, if the grafted larvae are infected, they may not die until they are extended in the cell after the cells are sealed. The greatest danger comes when queens are reared from colonies infected with sacbrood; then the tendency to the disease is accentuated in the resulting generations. The remedy is to requeen colonies infected with sacbrood and never rear any queens from colonies whose brood shows any evidence of this disease. This same precaution applies to the foulbrood diseases.

BREEDING FOR RESISTANCE

Research and practical experience over a period of many years have demonstrated that strains of bees can be selected and bred for disease resistance. Development of resistance requires continual selection and testing of possible breeding queens with the disease factor in mind. Careful observations have to be made of the brood of a breeding queen even after she has been selected as a breeder, for in some cases the susceptibility of her brood to some diseases does not show up until favorable environmental conditions are encountered. This delayed reaction may also be caused by the multiple mating of a queen and the manner in which the resulting sperms come into use.

Unfortunately, every location is not suited for selective breeding or control of drones, and the resistant factor may be sharply reduced if daughter queens mate with drones from colonies susceptible to disease.

CHEMICAL POISONING

Under certain conditions, the larvae in grafted cell cups turn dark and die within a day or two after being grafted. This has happened where fermented syrups are stored or fed in metal containers. The fermenting syrups dissolve enough of the metal to cause the death of the larvae.

Usually, however, the queen larvae are protected from such poisoning since the nurse bees die when they attempt to elaborate royal jelly from contaminated pollen or use contaminated syrup. It is very difficult to get a queen reared in a colony that has been severely injured by chemical poisoning or that has contaminated pollen in its comb.

Adult Queen Diseases

ACARAPIS MITES

Queens are said to be susceptible to infection, with *Acarapis woodi* Linn., the cause of acarine disease of bees. If they are not infected before they are mated, the chances are good that they will not become infected thereafter. The mites prefer young bees and apparently are unable to penetrate the prothoracic tracheae of older bees. External mites *A. dorsalis* and *A. externus* also have been reported as infesting queens, but the authors have not observed any queens infested with external mites. Fortunately, the internal mite has never been found in the United States, Canada, or Mexico.

The external mites apparently cause little or no injury to the bees they infest. No treatment is necessary.

AMOEBA DISEASE

A one-celled animal parasite that invades the ventriculus or mid-gut and the Malpighian tubules of adult bees causes amoeba disease. This parasite, *Vahlkampfia* (*Malpighamoeba*) *mellificae* Prell, has been found in various parts of the world but is seldom of much economic importance. Little is known of its life history or method of treatment.

BEE PARALYSIS

Paralysis is generally associated with the workers of a queen rather than with the queen herself. Queens reared from larvae of infected colonies produce colonies that have a tendency to be paralytic. Since the tendency toward paralysis appears to be caused by inherited factors, the mating of a queen with drones from paralytic colonies may cause susceptibility to paralysis in new workers.

Some types of paralysis have been determined as being caused by a virus. Other paralytic symptoms may be confused with various plant or chemical poisons.

Preventive measures are more effective than treatment. Queens should never be reared from colonies showing any evidence of paralysis. All drones from paralytic colonies should be killed and such colonies should be requeened as soon as the ailment is discovered. Commercial queen breeders in particular should observe these preventive measures.

The liberal application of powdered sulphur over the tops of the brood frames and in front of the entrances of colonies affected with paralysis sometimes aids in reducing the number of infected bees. The dead should be cleared from in front of the infected hive.

MELANOSIS

Orosi-Pal [2] found melanosis to be produced by a fungus, *Melanosella mors apis,* that caused the ovaries of bees, both workers and queens, to degenerate and turn black. The fungus also attacks oviducts and spermathecae, and is occasionally found in the mid-intestine and hind-intestine. There is no known treatment. Only microscopic examination of ailing queens can reveal this disease. Apparently it is not of common occurrence.

Another melanosis occurs in queens inseminated with semen apparently contaminated with bacteria from fecal matter of the drones or the queen. The bacteria multiply rapidly, turning the oviducts black, and the queen dies within a few hours or a day or two thereafter.

THE BEE "LOUSE"

The parasite *Braula coeca* Nitzsch is not a louse but a small wingless fly that lays its eggs beneath the surface of honey cappings and whose larvae form tunnels beneath the cappings. Small holes are left in the cappings as the adults emerge to congregate on the bees. The tunnels

---

[2] Orosi-Pal, Z. 1951. As reported by C. Toumanoff in Les Maladies des abeilles, La Revue Française d'Apiculture. 68, special number, pp. 281–84.

are visible from the surface of the cappings and spoil the appearance
of comb honey.

The adults show a marked preference for the queen, and are generally found between the bases of the wings and the legs. When disturbed, they will run over the queen's thorax.

The bee louse does not pierce the body of the bee for its nourishment, but takes food from the mouth of its host. As many as 75 individual parasites have been reported as being present on one queen.
It is not of common occurrence in this country, but is common in some
areas of Brazil.

NOSEMA DISEASE

The honey bee is parasitized by a protozoan, *Nosema apis* Rennie,
that invades the epithelial cells of the ventriculus or mid-gut, gradually reducing the efficiency of the mid-intestine in the digestion and
absorption of food. The effect on the individual bee is determined by
the amount or degree of infection; shortening of the life of the individual worker by a few days to a week is common. Queens may become
infected from the contaminated mouth parts of the nurse bees. Infection is apparently a matter of chance, for queens may be present in
infected colonies for a year or more without becoming contaminated.

The development of the organism within the individual bee has
been studied, but the factors that cause the rapid development of the
spores are still largely unknown. The spores are spread from bee to
bee by various means, generally by the contamination of the combs
when unfavorable weather confines infected bees to their hives for long
periods of time. If the infected bees are confined on stores having a
large amount of indigestible materials, dysentery may result because of
the accumulation of the waste products, and additional bees will become infected when they clean the combs. Nosema is not the primary
cause of dysentery, however. The temporary confinement of bees on
good stores, as in migratory beekeeping or in the shipment of package
bees, does not cause dysentery or a widespread increase in nosema
disease.

If queens become infected from the contaminated mouth parts of
nurse bees, they throw off spores of the parasite. This might be a minor
cause of disease spread in the colony. The speed with which the
disease develops in the queen depends on many factors, including the

degree of the initial infection, temperature conditions, and her general physiological condition. The ultimate effect, when the disease develops in a majority of the epithelial cells of the ventriculus, is that of starvation, causing the ovaries to be reduced in efficiency and to degenerate from lack of proper nourishment. The end result is supersedure—if environmental conditions are right—and in the ultimate death of the queen.

The examination of 2,088 laying queens taken from colonies at the time of requeening indicated an infection of 1 per cent, of which 76 per cent were only lightly infected. Queens that were artificially fed over one million spores of nosema were still laying regularly and without any evidence of the disease at the end of three weeks. Of 209 queens held in infected colonies for an average of 25 days, 12 became infected, of which eight were only lightly infected. The colonies in which the queens were held had an average infection of 56 per cent. These results indicate that the infection of queen bees with nosema spores is the result of chance and that, while nosema disease may contribute to the supersedure of queens, it is by no means the primary cause of supersedure. Many other factors, such as malnutrition, faulty mating, cold, over heating, and physical injury can cause supersedure and undoubtedly do to a greater extent than nosema disease.

Nosema disease tends to disappear with continued warm weather and under conditions when the bees can have regular cleansing flights, as during the spring and summer. The disease is less prevalent in warm areas than where bees are confined by inclement weather, but is of world-wide distribution. It probably can be found in a majority of all apiaries if a sufficient number of bees are examined. Too much emphasis should not be placed on its presence in a colony or apiary without qualifying information as to the degree of infection and the economic importance of the level of infection.

Control. Probably one of the best methods of control of nosema is to maintain good stores in all colonies during long periods of confinement by bad weather. This applies particularly in the colder portions of this country and when package bees are established on drawn combs during cold weather.

Since the disease has the tendency to build up in old bees, the elimination of old bees from nuclei, queen banks, or queen-holding colonies will tend to reduce the possibility of infection. Such colonies should be fed only on good honey or heavy sugar syrup, not on a poor grade of honey. Only young nurse bees should be placed in mailing cages with queens.

The proper feeding of the antibiotic fumagillin, sold as Fumidil-B, will tend to reduce the incidence of the disease. But beekeepers have to decide on the economics of its use. The usual recommendation is to feed 189.3 mg. of active fumagillin in each gallon of syrup and to feed at weekly intervals at about the time the first samples of bees show evidence of nosema.

A microscopic examination of the ventriculus of a bee or of the fecal deposits of a living queen will show evidence of the disease. Identification by the gross appearance of the ventriculus is not reliable and the behavior symptoms of bees at the entrance can be confused with other causes of abnormal behavior.

Bailey,[3] of Rothamsted, found that the disease can be carried over winter on contaminated brood combs and that the transfer of infected colonies to clean combs or combs fumigated with glacial acetic acid for 24 hours had a beneficial effect.

The incidence of the disease in an infected colony falls in summer almost to the vanishing point, and may then build up again in the fall, winter, and spring if no control measures are used. The strengthening of weakened colonies a few weeks before the beginning of the honey flow helps to reduce the effects of nosema disease.

NON-LAYING QUEENS

Not infrequently queens that show evidence of having been mated do not begin to lay in a normal manner. Dissections of a number of such queens have indicated either a stoppage of the common oviduct with dried sperm or other foreign material, or some organic abnormality of the queen. In one case that came to the authors' attention, there was no connection between the ovaries and the common oviduct of the ailing queen.

NON-HATCHING QUEEN EGGS

In some instances, all or a large portion of the eggs layed by an apparently normal queen do not hatch. In such instances it is probable

---

[3] Bailey, L. 1955. The epidemiology and control of Nosema disease of the honeybee. Ann. Appl. Biol. 43:3, 379–89.

that the physiology of the queen is such that she cannot provide adequate nourishment for the nurse cells in the ovaries, so the embryo in the egg cannot reach the larval stage. Undoubtedly some organic deficiency in the queen is responsible, not the pollen in the area, for it is seldom that more than one queen out of several hundred is so affected.

Hitchcock[4] observed 5 out of 15 queens received, from the same queen breeder, whose eggs did not hatch. One of the queens laid non-hatching eggs for three and one-half months, while the population of her colony was maintained by the addition of brood or bees from normal colonies. He found on close observation that a very small percentage of her eggs did hatch, producing workers as well as drones. After reviewing the literature on the subject and after allowing the queens to lay under varying conditions, he concluded that the true cause of the abnormality was unknown.

Toxins in the pollen of the California Buckeye elaborated into brood food by the nurse bees affects the physiology of the queen. She progressively becomes a drone layer, then lays many eggs which do not hatch or whose larvae die within 12 to 24 hours after hatching. Some few that do reach maturity may be unable to shed the last pupal skin or are deformed.

In other instances, some eggs lack viability and do not hatch or produce larvae which die at an early age. The situation is generally due to inherited lethal factors resulting from inbreeding. The most obvious result is brood spotted with many empty cells instead of the compact brood pattern of desirable queens.

"Epilepsis"

Many beekeepers have had the experience when handling queens of having an occasional queen stiffen up and fall over on her side as if she had been stung. She remains motionless for several minutes. This type of behavior is generally called "epilepsis," as it appears to be a convulsion caused by some nervous shock. If the queen in this condition is placed on the top bar of a comb in her hive, she will gradually become active and apparently recovers without any evidence of impairment.

---

[4] Hitchcock, J. D. 1956. Honeybee queens whose eggs all fail to hatch. Jour. Econ. Ent. 49:1, 11–14.

Some Anomalies of Queens

Occasionally queens occur with certain organic abnormalities that are difficult to explain. "Humpbacked" queens, with an enlarged thorax and a compressed head, have been taken from cells, usually beyond the period of emergence. Other queens in the same lot of cells are generally normal.

Queens with part worker and part queen features, or with some male structures, are sometimes seen, mostly in nursery cages. These could be due to some inherited mutant character.

Queens have been reared with white eyes or eyes of different colors than normal. Such peculiarities are caused by genetic factors.

By selection for eye color, one could develop a strain with queens, drones, or workers having white or red eyes, or eyes of other colors. However, the lighter eye pigments or lack of pigment affects bee vision, and such strains would not be entirely desirable. Red- or brown-eyed bees are little, if any, handicapped by their eye color.

Some queens produce progeny with various malformations or anomolies, such as deficiencies in body structures, crinkled wings that make it impossible for the workers to fly, a lack of antennae or mouth parts, a variation in the shape and size of the head, or some combinations of these characters. Drones with eyes of different color, cycloptic drones or workers, gynandromorphs or portions of both sexes in the same bee, and many other variations have been observed. Most of these are due to genetic factors operating during the maturation or development of the egg. They are not common but are of great scientific interest.

Index

Acarapis mites, 154
Ailments of queens, 152–160
Alleles, 123–124; multiple, 124
Alley, Henry, 9, 10, 11, 47; method of queen rearing, 10, 11, 47–48, 64
American Bee Journal, 5, 9, 12
American foulbrood, 37, 152–153
Amoeba disease, 154
Anaesthetics, for insemination, 140, 142, 144, 145
Anatomy of the honeybee, 2, 12
Aristotle, 1–3
Artificial cell cups, 10, 12, 33, 51, 53–55
Artificial insemination, 12, 137–151; instruments, 138–144; methods, 144–147
Assortment, independent, 125

Baby nuclei, 11, 15, 78, 85, 90; early use of, 3; management of, 90–95
Bacillus larvae, 152
Bailey, L., 158
Balling queens, 100
Barber pipette manipulator, 140
Bee house for queen rearing, 76–80
Bee "louse" (*Braula coeca*), 155
Beekeeping, early progress in America, 5–13
Bees: Caucasian, 18; developmental stages, 20; inheritance in, 14, 113–136; Italian, 4, 8, 18; judging of, 14, 29–31, 133; number in mating colonies, 84; nurse, 21, 66; races of, 4, 8, 18; sex of, 2, 4, 14–15, 120–121
Benton, Frank, 9
Berlepach, Baron von, 4, 5
Bertholf, L. M., 19
Beven, Edward, 2
Bishop, George, 138

Black bees of Silesia, 4
Bonnet, Charles, 2–3
Boyd, W. L., 10
Braula coeca, 155
Breeder queens, 29, 31, 135; classification of, 28; selection of, 29, 43, 135–136
Breeding: and stock improvement, 113–136; defined, 113; for resistance, 153; goal of, 128; program for commercial beekeeper, 132–136; stock testing, 133
Brood, 67, 133–134; diseases, 152–153; food glands, 32; rearing, 26
Brooks, J. M., 10
Brunnich, Dr., 137
Burnens, Francis, 3
Butler, Charles, 2
Butler, C. G., 112

Cage: nursery, 9, 11, 81–82, 104; queen introducing, 104, 106; queen mailing, 9, 105–106; robber, 96–97
Cale, G. H., 139
California Buckeye, 159
Caligula, 2
Callow, R. W., 112
Candling of queen cells, 80
Candy, queen cage, 9, 34, 36
Carbon dioxide: anaesthetic, 140, 142, 144–145; hasten queen laying, 149
Care: of inseminated queens, 150; of queens, 99–100; of queen cells, 80
Carniolan bees, 18
Cary, 8
Catching queens, 102–103
Caucasian bees, 18, 29
Cell bar frames, 55
Cell bars, 10, 55, 57
Cell-building colonies, 11–12, 41, 63–75,